MATH CLASS REDESIGNED

HOW TO TEACH CHILDREN TO LOVE MATH

JANE MOLNAR

ISBN-13: 978-1-7327374-0-2

CONTENTS

1

DROPPING BY A CLASS

Imagine that you want your child to learn the piano. In fact, this matters to you so much that you decide to take things to the extreme. You sign your child up for lessons five days a week, with a requirement of daily practice. Not only are you very excited, but your music-loving child is eager to begin.

To your dismay, several weeks pass and your child has made no meaningful progress with the piano and even seems to have come to hate the mere mention of pianos. Sometimes you listen near the door while your child is practicing. Nothing about the sounds coming from the piano suggests your child is even taking piano lessons, let alone going every day. If you go in and try to help, your child fusses, protests, gets mad, and cries.

You decide you must take time off work to go and see what is going on with the piano lessons. Standing in the doorway, this is what you observe:

There are thirty fidgety children in the room, all looking in different directions. The teacher is standing at the front of the room talking about pianos and drawing piano keys on the board. You find your mind wandering over and over. You had not realized you were so hungry when you set out and you keep thinking about whether you might be able to get a cup of coffee and a pastry on your way back to work. You cannot remember a time since you graduated from high school when you felt more bored but you force yourself to stand still and listen, wrenching your attention back again and again to what the teacher is saying about keys and notes.

The children are also having trouble focusing. Some are talking to each other and others are staring into space. A plump boy with very short light brown hair is reading a novel he has balanced in his lap behind his desk. Several children are playing games surreptitiously on their phones. A skinny boy in high-tops is experimenting with how far back he can tilt his chair without falling over backwards. A freckled girl is slowly dipping pretzels into a small container of artificial cheese. Her friend is making a chain of paperclips.

At last the teacher tells the children to break up into groups of five and brainstorm about playing the piano. You'd be hard-pressed to summarize the last twenty minutes, even though you play the piano quite well yourself.

On bright yellow paper, Piano Problem of the Week is being passed out to everyone. It reads: On Wednesday a boy named Sam wants to play five chords on two different pianos without playing the same notes twice while his friend Bob wants to play two scales on three pianos (and can play a note more than once). What will be the highest note played or can it be determined?

"Be sure to record your strategies in your Piano Journals," the teacher says. "I want to see full sentences."

Quietly, trying not to draw attention to yourself, you slip along the side of the room to the back and eavesdrop on one of the groups. This is what you hear:

"You do the writing."

"We're all supposed to write."

"I ain't writing about no pianos!"

"Come on. Let's just get it over with."

"What is it we're supposed to be doing?"

"Piano strategies."

"What is a piano strategy?'

"I don't know! Let's just put something."

You peer over and see one child has laboriously written:

Pianoes are good. Pianoes have keys, There is middel c. it is in the middel. Pianoes are instramints. And so are viohlins.

Another child, leaning over and reading it too, accuses sharply, "That's not a strategy! That's just a bunch of words."

Crushed and annoyed, the child who did the writing replies, "It's a lot better than your blank journal."

Another child asks, "What about the Piano Problem of the Week?"

"That's all about chords. What is a chord anyway?"

"I don't know!"

"Me neither. Let's just say chords are good too."

Looking up, you notice your own child is dueling with pencils across the room.

~

We would never tolerate this for our child's piano lessons.

Yet we do for math.

Even if this piano lesson were improved and the children were marched off to a gym full of pianos, told to watch the teacher play, and then told to play the pianos themselves and record their findings, most would still learn next to nothing. A child with a rare talent might sit down and play what the teacher played by ear – but most would just tap or bang or write on the keys or play a few notes or even pry up a key. The mastering of scales, the reading of music, the positioning of hands and wrists, the correct fingering ... most of it would never come.

We all seem to know instinctively what will work with piano lessons even though most of us could not teach one well, if at all: first of all, our child needs a skilled teacher, highly recommended by other parents. That teacher needs to provide direct instruction to our child, watching our child's hands, listening to our child playing, playing for our child, assigning work suited to our child, checking the progress on all the details that make for good playing – fingering and timing and touch and posture, reading music, playing by ear, doing scales, memorizing pieces, putting feeling into the playing, learning music theory. That teacher needs to correct gently before bad habits get set and inspire our child with new pieces played beautifully, encouraging, stretching our child at times right to the edge of what our child is capable of, and at other times letting her play pieces she can play perfectly so she feels masterful. No one would even think of kidding themselves that a long series of group discussions about pianos between nine-year-olds who don't know how to play the piano might lead to piano mastery or even piano progress. Our common sense would rear up and tell us not to waste our child's time and our money.

Yet our common sense fails us when it comes to math.

How has this happened?

Most children start kindergarten eager to learn math, full of enthusiasm. In the beginning, they sing out numbers with joy. They count for pleasure. If you ask a small child what two plus five is, he will exuberantly tell you it is seven, as if he is delivering good news — the good news that there are these delightful things, numbers, that relate to each other in dependable ways, and the further even better news that the child is in on this and knows the answer to your question.

What happens to all that potential, that enthusiasm, that eagerness? Why are so many children able to master the complexities of running, talking, reading, writing, arguing persuasively (at times almost *too* persuasively), playing video games with astonishing coordination, swimming, descending flights of steps or even handrails on skateboards, and playing musical instruments — yet fail to learn how to solve math problems with anything remotely close to the same level of skill and competence?

The majority of children who start school eager and optimistic end up mathematically damaged, functioning far below their capability level.

In this book, I will explore why this happens and propose solutions that can be put into place by ordinary teachers working in ordinary schools. It would be nice if the country educated and paid and respected teachers as if they were as important as doctors or lawyers (which in my view they are), but this book is intended to offer immediate solutions, most of which can be implemented right away, without such enormous and unlikely changes happening first.

2

WHY DO THINGS GO SO WRONG?

Why do children who start out so eager and capable in kindergarten end up wasting so much of their time over a period of thirteen years in school and often turn out mathematically incompetent?

I have identified twenty common math teaching practices which undermine and sabotage children's potential love of math and their mathematical development. In further chapters, I explore why these practices are damaging, and, in each case, offer a more effective teaching practice.

Here are the misguided teaching practices:

1. Missing the main point of a math class which should be to instill a deep and abiding love of math in children;
2. Not requiring children to solve nearly enough problems to achieve mastery;
3. Not taking into account how children naturally learn;
4. Requiring an entire class of children to work on the same material at the same pace, regardless of their level of proficiency and current aptitude, thus ensuring that if the class is made of up children at significantly different

levels (as almost all public school classes are), many or most of the children will not make any meaningful progress;

5. Delaying offering children irresistible and beautiful math until after the children have firmly made up their minds that math is tedious and boring;
6. Failing to create a classroom atmosphere of deep respect for everyone in the class, including the most struggling and the most advanced children;
7. An over-emphasis on elaborate, expensive, time-consuming testing which does not directly benefit the children being tested;
8. Trying to build on a weak foundation: a lack of frequent, quick, non-stressful assessments to determine what material will best serve each child in the class and ensure that every child builds a solid foundation;
9. A lack of immediate feedback for teachers, while they are presenting material at the board, from all the students in the room on whether they are understanding what is being taught;
10. A lack of immediate on-going feedback for children, while they are solving problems at their desks or at home, on whether they are grasping the material they are working on;
11. The awkward, confusing presentation of topics which can be conveyed in simple, straightforward ways;
12. A failure to present standard algorithms clearly and directly in elementary school and require students to master them;
13. Using visually cluttered textbooks and worksheets;
14. A failure to require children to memorize math facts which are necessary for success in later math classes;
15. An over-emphasis on group work in situations where it serves no useful propose and hinders learning;
16. An under-utilization of one of a classroom's best resources: peer teachers;

17. A lack of discovery-based learning in situations where it instills joy, confidence and curiosity and an insistence on discovery-based learning in situations where it creates confusion and frustration;
18. Forcing children to explain how they arrived at their answers in full sentences on paper;
19. Insisting that children show particular steps on paper after they have already solved a problem correctly without taking these steps;
20. Mixing math with other tasks in a way that compromises both the learning of math and the accomplishment of the other tasks.

3

THE PRIMARY GOAL: INSTILLING A DEEP LOVE OF MATH

The primary goal of a math class should be to instill a deep love of math in every child in the room. When children really love an activity, they devote themselves to it. They focus. They pour their time and energy into it. They question. They persevere. They explore. They practice. If they make a mistake, they figure out what went wrong and try again.

Conversely, when children dislike something, they are ingenious at coming up with endless ways to delay or avoid doing it, to pretend to do it while not really doing it, or to do it in the most slap-dash way possible.

How can a love of math be instilled? How can we harness the natural curiosity and passion for learning that all very young children have and open them up to the beauty of mathematics? How can we avoid doing the things that are almost guaranteed to make children recoil or shut down from math in boredom and frustration?

We need to make math deeply engaging and satisfying. We need to present it in a way that is both playful and rigorous. We need to reveal its beauty long before children begin to withdraw from it. Children need to experience the richness and power of math right from the start.

When we plan each day's math lesson, the guiding principle needs to be: how can I make the math irresistible to every child in the class? How can I draw in all the children so they focus so intensely they forget about everything but math for an hour? How can I make them feel exhilarated, inspired, and satisfied yet wanting more?

4

NO SUBSTITUTE FOR SOLVING PROBLEMS

No one enjoys an activity he knows little to nothing about, finds confusing, and never gets any better at despite months or even years of trying. In order to enjoy math, one has to make progress and become increasingly competent at it.

There is only one way to become confident and capable at math: by successfully solving thousands and thousands of varied and increasingly difficult problems over a period of many years. Math is learned by actually doing it. There is great value in a clear explanation and in certain types of discussion about math, but ultimately, one has to pick up a pencil, all on one's own, and solve problems independently.

There is no substitute for this, and all attempts to get around this will end in disappointment and failure.

When educators and politicians attempt to solve the problem of North American children doing so badly in math, they tend to overlook the simplest and most practical solutions. Instead, committees are gathered and standards are re-written. Success is redefined and, at tremendous expense, new tests are created to attempt to measure this redefined success. Millions of existing textbooks are suddenly of no use and new ones need to be written and purchased by school districts. Homework is increased. More is demanded of parents. Meetings are held to help parents understand their role in overseeing homework that leaves their children in tears of frustration. New manipulatives are purchased and old manipulatives lugged out and put in storage rooms. Algorithms are withdrawn from the curriculum for a few years, then put back in, requiring yet more replacing of textbooks. Overhead projectors are rolled in. Blackboards are replaced with whiteboards. Math journals are purchased and given to children to fill with their thoughts about math.

Yet none of this makes much difference. Most children continue to function far below their capability level.

Why?

The real problem is that math is not being taught in a way that leads children to love it, and children are not solving anything close to the number of math problems they would need to solve in order to become proficient. These two things need to come hand in hand: a deepening love of math, and the solving of vast numbers of problems.

5

HOW DO CHILDREN NATURALLY LEARN?

In order to create a class that results in children loving math, we need to take into account how children naturally learn. We need to harness the tremendous energy children have and use this energy and curiosity and wonder to drive their math education. We also need to understand what causes children to dig in their heels and resist and, whenever possible, we need to avoid doing the things which trigger this response.

How do children really like to learn? When do they learn most swiftly? And what educational experiences do they tend to resist or even loathe? Are these loathed experiences valuable enough to be worth a prolonged struggle?

Children learn primarily by doing, not by listening to or watching other people do things. They are happiest when they are busy — and by busy, I do not mean frenetically active, I mean engaged, including engaged in pondering.

Most children greatly prefer interactive science museums over museums where they are only permitted to observe. Most children would not want to listen to a long chemistry lecture — but they love to do chemistry experiments, even ones in which the experiment is clearly laid out and they need to record their findings systematically.

Children like to build things, design things, test things. They learn by playing and experimenting.

They like to understand things, and show that they understand them.

Most children do not like to listen to long, detailed instructions. They don't like being made to sit and listen to things they already know, or being made to do things repeatedly which they have already mastered. They don't like sitting still for long periods unless they are so absorbed in something they have forgotten they're sitting still. Many children actually prefer getting in trouble over feeling bored.

When it comes to math, what does *doing* really mean? It does not mean that children have to rush outside and build a fence, measuring the boards first (though that might be fun and useful) in order to learn arithmetic.

What it does mean is that children need to be at the helm of their mathematical experience, actively solving problems as independently as possible. The children may be stiller than they've been all day, and quieter than one could imagine them being —but they need to be intensely engaged when it comes to solving the problems at hand.

Children like structure and a predictable routine, yet they do not like any limits placed on their learning. We need to create an orderly classroom environment that is focused, joyful, respectful, and non-competitive. Within this safe and peaceful structure, we should offer children an unlimited number of math problems, as well as help at any level it is needed, from the most basic to the most advanced.

6

EVERY CHILD NEEDS MATH AT HER REAL LEVEL

For math to be enjoyable and satisfying to a child, the material needs to be accessible and challenging. Math that is out of a child's reach is frustrating and distressing. Math that is too easy is tedious and stultifying. Every child in the class needs to be given math that is at her real level, and it should never be assumed that a child's real level corresponds to her grade level. Often it doesn't. In many classrooms, most of the children are working on the wrong level of material most of the time, struggling with problems they lack the foundation to solve or stagnating in concepts they have already mastered.

Many educators think it is best to define each grade level of math as being composed of a set of concepts and hold everyone in the room to this definition of appropriate math for the year. The following year, the child is advanced on to the next grade level in math even if he has failed to grasp much or most of the preceding grade's material. If a child learns 40% of the material in fourth grade, he is allowed a fresh start in fifth grade. He begins the same fifth-grade material as a child who had learned 95% of the fourth-grade material and both children are expected to move along at the same pace.

Because so much of mathematics is sequential, this is disastrous. There are certain critical concepts and procedures which are necessary for advancing in math. If a child can only add by counting on his fingers, learning multiplication will be terribly cumbersome. If a child has not mastered fractions, large parts of algebra will be hopelessly confusing. If a child can't divide numbers, polynomial long division will make no sense at all.

Advancing children to the next level before they have mastered the necessary foundational concepts almost guarantees that the longer a struggling child stays in school, the worse he will do in math. It also means that higher grades will have many more failing children in them.

Public school math classes typically contain an enormous range of levels of math proficiency. If we treat an entire class of children as if they are all at the same level and try to get them to learn a set of pre-determined topics, we fail to meet the needs of most of them. When children are asked to solve problems and take tests on material they lack the background to understand, the result is usually frustration, confusion, embarrassment, and, quite often, poor behavior and an apparent inability to focus. Some children genuinely have ADHD; others have a situationally-triggered inability to focus. They are being asked, over and over, to attend to tasks they lack the skills to succeed at and they respond by humming, banging, poking others with pencils, or doing anything else they can think of to relieve the very unpleasant sensations of inadequacy, shame, and boredom. Given the right level of math and the right support and feedback, all this humming and banging and poking will, for many children, come to an abrupt halt.

Denying a child more advanced math when she has mastered her grade's topics is equally damaging and can result in behavior problems as well. When children are obliged to work below or above their real level, they learn very little, are prone to distract others, and can develop a lasting dislike for math.

We need to let go of the outdated goal (which was somewhat understandable, though still damaging, in the days before the internet) of getting every child in the room to work on a set of pre-determined topics.

This goal should be replaced by a higher and much more practical goal: to engage every child in the class at the highest level possible for that child for the entire length of every math period.

The focus should not be on uniformity, but rather on maximizing every child's growth and pleasure in math.

~

Suppose, in a fourth-grade class, Andy is still confused about carrying and borrowing, while Tanisha is ready for trigonometry. Each of these children's needs is pressing and urgent. Neither child should be focusing primarily on fourth-grade math.

If Andy, over the course of the year, can master all the concepts he did not learn in first, second, and third grades (or even half of these), he will be much better off than if he is pressed to struggle with fourth-grade topics, some of which he might be able to memorize without understanding and others of which he will be so confused by that he won't be able to get any traction with them at all. If the teacher takes the attitude that nothing can go too wrong with Tanisha, the highly advanced student, because she is so far ahead, and at most Tanisha should be offered a few enrichment problems which may take her a little deeper into the same math the rest of the class is doing, Tanisha will not thrive either. Just like the struggling Andy, she needs math at her level.

If the teacher notices that a child in the class has advanced to a level beyond the teacher and the teacher can no longer offer meaningful help when the child gets stuck, this should not be a signal that the child needs to hold back on learning. Instead, the child should be offered more and more challenging math, and — if this is possible — the teacher should invite a volunteer parent, university student, or member of the community who has a deep love and grasp of math to come into the classroom during math period and offer help and inspiration to the most advanced math students.

Many parents, even very busy ones, would relish the chance to make a real difference in a classroom and play a significant role in the learning process and would actually prefer this to making cupcakes or a financial donation. There are also many people in the community, including retired scientists or engineers or mathematicians, who like being connected to young people and would very much enjoy being of great service for an hour a day and making a huge difference to some children. As well as offering inspiration and instruction to students whose math level is beyond that of the classroom teacher, these volunteers could also provide individual help to any struggling child who needs it.

The most efficient way I have found to provide every child in a classroom with the appropriate level of math is by using Khan Academy. Khan Academy's free website allows students to zero in on their level and work through problem sets which cover math topics from kindergarten through calculus. This makes it possible to tailor the level of math to the needs of the students in a way that would otherwise take hours of preparation each day on the part of the teacher. While the students are working on Khan Academy, the teacher can move around the room, guiding and helping.

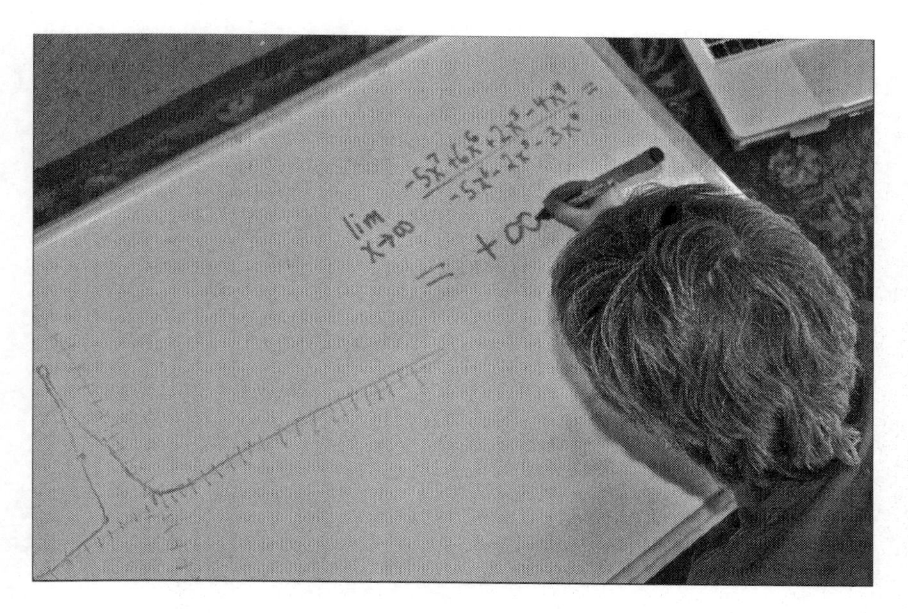

ten-year-old solving Khan Academy calculus problems

7

PACE OF LEARNING

Not only are the children in a public-school classroom often at a wide range of different levels in math, they also learn at markedly different rates.

The pace at which a child learns math is affected by a variety of factors which can be broken down into six main categories:

1. Level of mathematical competence

- mastery of prerequisite concepts
- automaticity with math facts
- mastery of standard algorithms
- problem-solving skills

2. Past experiences with math

- quality of past math teachers
- past experiences with math
- mathematical confidence

- interest in the subject

3. Support system

- people able and willing to help the child every day with homework if help is needed

4. Brain impairment from past traumas

- past drug use
- traumatic brain injuries from football and other sports, or from accidents or abuse
- brain damage from the parents' drug and alcohol use prior to the child's birth

5. Cognitive impairment from immediate factors

- drug use immediately before or during math class
- level of psychological distress
- how much sleep the child had the night before
- degree of hunger

6. Appropriateness of the math for the child

- is there a match between the child's level and the material being offered

A ninth grader who is confident, rested, fed, and has had the good fortune to have had a series of excellent math teachers, did not suffer any brain damage in utero, does not use drugs himself, and memorized his math facts in third grade and knows how to multiply and divide swiftly, may absorb a new concept more than a hundred times faster than a classmate whose brain was damaged by his mother's drug and alcohol use during pregnancy, has been pushed along from year to year without ever mastering critical concepts, sustained two concussions during last football season, considers himself bad at math, smokes marijuana every day, went to bed at 2 am, and did not eat breakfast.

This enormous range of learning speeds is often brushed aside in school and most children are made to work more slowly than suits them or rushed on to new material before they are ready for it. By failing to meet the needs of struggling children and pretending they are learning faster than they really are, we lead them to fall further and further behind. Instead, we should be teaching them the specific skills they failed to master in earlier grades, allowing them to practice these skills to the point of automaticity, and increasing their confidence and competence. Simultaneously, they should be offered interesting grade-level problems which do not depend on skills they lack.

Repeated experiences of failure give children a sense of hopelessness. Instead of standing back and letting a fifteen-year-old with a fourth-grade proficiency level go through the entirely predictable and humiliating experience of failing algebra, we should be giving him a series of increasingly difficult problems at his level which he can succeed at. Repeated experiences of success alter the way children approach and solve math problems just as powerfully as repeated experiences of failure do.

Lagging, struggling students are capable of vastly more than most people assume — but they will not reach their potential unless they are offered direct instruction at their real level and at the right pace.

8

IRRESISTIBLE MATH

Young children love solving problems that are mathematically interesting. Oddly, these sorts of problems are usually withheld from children until they have already come to dislike math and believe that it is boring.

The time to start interesting math is in first grade (or sooner) — not instead of arithmetic, but in addition to arithmetic. We need to let children in on the beauty of math before they pull away from it. It's never too late to see the beauty, but it is much easier to see it before the mind creates a dense web of associations between math and boredom.

And even arithmetic, if it is taught right, is beautiful.

What makes children pull away from math and decide they don't like it? Boredom, intense frustration, shame, and a sense that math is dry and tedious now and always will be.

And what about the beauty? What *is* mathematical beauty and how can we offer it to children?

The beauty of math lies in its patterns and symmetries, its order and connections, its paradoxes, its mysterious presence in sunflowers and galaxies and pinecones, its vastness, its satisfactions, its neatness and precision, its power. It is pressingly urgent that we let young children in on this right from the very start.

Many parts of math build upon other parts, making it hard to grasp these areas if one has missed key concepts. The sequential learning involved is rather like climbing a ladder. If four rungs are missing, it's very difficult to keep ascending. An equation like $x^2 + 5x + 6 = 0$ is an example of a problem which requires mastering a sequence of skills in order to make sense of it and solve it efficiently.

There is, however, a trove of interesting math problems which children can dive into without having already memorized math facts or mastered arithmetic algorithms or learned a long sequence of concepts which build upon each other. Rather than being "ladder climbing math," one could think of this as a flat landscape of "stepping stone math," approachable from many levels and angles. This kind of math can be used to draw children into the beauty of math very early, and it can also be used to keep struggling children engaged. These topics can have an equalizing effect in the classroom because they can be offered to the entire class, regardless of the wide span of proficiency and mastery levels. An example of this would be the Königsberg Bridge Problem and variations on it. (In this problem, one must determine if it is possible to cross the seven bridges that connect parts of a city without retracing one's steps.)

A job which required irresistible math

In 1990, after ten years of math teaching (first at a college and then for the nonprofit Project SEED which sent mathematicians and scientists into inner-city classrooms), I began teaching math independently, meaning I did not work for any school or district or organization. I was paid directly by the parents of the children in my classes which I offered after school in a number of public schools in Berkeley. This gave me tremendous freedom, but it also meant that if I failed to make the math compelling, my new teaching venture would fail.

My single goal was to get children to deeply understand and love math. My income, I knew, would depend entirely on whether I met this goal. My partners in success would be the children in my classes. If they begged their parents to be allowed to come to my math classes, few parents would say, "No, I'm afraid you may not stay after school to do an extra hour and a half of math. Definitely not." I had to make my classes so engaging that the children who had an array of after-school options such as chess and ceramics and African dance and soccer and ballet would choose math instead.

If my classes were boring, word would spread quickly and I would soon have very few pupils. I had to make the math irresistible from the very first lesson. I could not spend weeks laying the groundwork, teaching dry arithmetic which might one day come in handy. The enjoyment needed to start on the first day.

And the enjoyment had to last all year, and then all the next year, and the next. I wanted to keep my same students for many years. Prior to this, the longest I usually taught a child (other than a family member) was for one school year. I knew that there was really only one way to make sure every child in my classes loved them: have each child learn a great deal of math. I might be able to entertain them briefly with some games or lively discussions — but to keep them engaged indefinitely, I was going to have to offer much more than this (though I sometimes made use of games and lively discussions). I had to make sure every single child was intellectually stimulated and rapidly progressing.

This meant I had to come up with enough interesting problems to keep a class of fifteen to twenty-five children intensely engaged over a period of many years. Some of the children joined the class tremendously accomplished at arithmetic and others very weak at it. Now and then a profoundly gifted child signed up. I also had students with learning disabilities. Some children ended up staying in my classes for eight years (starting in first grade) and became phenomenally good at problem-solving and I had to keep them challenged. For these children, I had to offer lots of "ladder style" problems so they could build on their skills. I also had new children join my class in any of the grade levels I taught (first through eighth) and I had to provide enough accessible and enjoyable problems to draw them in, not have them feel intimidated in any way by the students who had been there for a long time, and keep them learning and engaged as well.

I began searching for math books I could use with my classes. I wanted books which were filled with the kinds of problems that children can't resist solving.

I soon realized there was not a single math book available that I could use for this purpose. I searched everywhere and kept on searching for years and years (and still search!) but every book I found had major drawbacks. Most were too boring. Who would want to come to my class after school to dip into a dry textbook or workbook if they could rush down the hall and put on an African costume and start dancing or pull on their cleats and play soccer or go home and play video games and eat potato chips?

Some books had a few good problems buried in them but most pages were not compelling to children. Even the best problems were usually presented in a way that was far too wordy. Children are not drawn to lengthy instructions. They like to jump right in.

Other books took a topic like fractions and covered it in great depth, but so dryly and relentlessly that most children would have rebelled. Most textbooks were huge and cluttered and repelled children. Though the internet had recently come into being, it did not yet give teachers access to troves of math problems for children.

My only option was to write the material myself. Luckily, my schedule allowed for this. Instead of rushing off to school by eight a.m., I could get up every morning, make my Irish Breakfast tea and toast with cherry jam, and spend as much time as was needed to come up with the afternoon's math.

I lived at that time right next to the U. C. Berkeley campus in a long 1920's apartment, one room wide and five rooms deep. Hours passed in what often felt like minutes as I came up with math problems that were designed to lead children from confusion to states of triumph. The apartment was perfectly quiet. I had four large desks to spread out my work on and I moved between these desks and a very comfortable blue armchair, writing and illustrating. Most of my classes covered a two-year age span, such as grades one and two, or grades four and five, but within each class, there could be a span of math levels that was far greater than two years. I had to come up with enough problems to keep both the fastest and the slowest children engaged for the whole class.

In the middle of the afternoon, I would set out for one of my schools (I went to a different one each day of the week) with the latest math problems in one hand and a huge canvas bag full of dozens of mathematical games in the other hand.

Unlike regular textbook writers who often have little or no contact with children in classrooms, I got to put my work to the test every day. Within a few hours of creating a set of problems, I would see which ones most appealed to children, which ones the children begged for more of, and which ones, if any, caused confusion. I could see if a word I had assumed everyone knew tripped up a few children, or if something was too easy – or too hard. I could test their limits for repetition. I had to give just enough problems of one type to lead to mastery, but not so many the children dug in their heels.

I did not want them to forget anything they had learned in my classes, so I had to build in review – but I had to build it in craftily. I had to disguise it, sometimes slightly and sometimes greatly.

I wanted my students to master the critical skill of spotting the familiar in the new. To teach them this, I had to embed the familiar in their work, mixing it up with new things to hone this skill in them and to keep up their interest.

In creating the hundreds of problem sets I made up over the next seven years, I did not have to please any educators, use any district materials, prepare students for any test, or teach concepts in any particular order. I could teach absolutely any math in any order and at any pace I chose, as long as my students were learning and loving it. If even one child was confused or bored, the class would not function smoothly, so I could not let this happen.

exuberant young algebra students

Providing every child in a class with a limitless supply of math problems at her level is an absolutely essential part of a successful math class. This meant I had to anticipate how far the very quickest students might go and prepare enough problems to keep them busy right up to the last second of class. I also had to bring problems that would transform the struggling students into confident, capable ones. I regarded every moment of class time as precious for every child.

There was never any requirement or even expectation that everyone in the class had to do all the problems I brought. The children were simply expected to work hard at whatever pace came naturally to them and to learn as much as possible.

When I handed out the work, the students would dive straight into it. They were so focused on what they were doing that they weren't paying any attention to whether someone else had done twice as many problems, or half as many. They just worked away and as soon as they had finished all the problems they had on their desk they would rush over to the table where I had arranged stacks of problem sets. They often helped each other but this was entirely their choice. They could ask for help from me or from each other whenever the need arose.

While I realise most math teachers will not have the luxury of having three blissfully quiet and uninterrupted hours to prepare a lesson, many will have one huge advantage which I did not have back in the days when I would spend so much time writing math problems: the internet, and more specifically, Khan Academy. In addition to this, I plan to create a series of workbooks of the math problems I gave to the children in my classes.

9

DIGNITY AND RESPECT

If we acknowledge that we should be providing every child in a classroom with math which is at just the right level, how can we preserve the dignity of children who are lacking grade-level skills while making sure they learn those skills? How can we avoid any kind of stigmatizing or humiliation of the students who have fallen behind their peers?

We need to change both the goal and the atmosphere of math class.

For starters, we need to show the deepest level of respect for every child in the room, including those who are years behind and those who are years beyond their peers. Showing respect entails seeing individual children for who they really are, nonjudgmentally and compassionately, showing them how much they matter by refusing to let them fall through the cracks, holding them to the high behavioral standards which are vital to a smoothly functioning classroom, and offering them exactly what they need in the moment in order to progress.

Our society has both of terror of and a taboo against acknowledging significant academic variation in the classroom, despite the fact that most classrooms contain enormous variation. Advanced students are often told, in one way or another, to bide their time and act more "ordinary". Struggling students are given a similar message and urged to appear more average by participating in a pretense that they are operating at a level far beyond the level they know is their present *real* level.

Common messages that are conveyed to the advanced student include: *slow down; stop being a brat; stop showing off; in case you thought you were special, you're not; no one has the time to keep up with you; getting you even further ahead is no one's priority here; your boredom is of no importance compared to the much more pressing needs of the rest of the class.*

The struggling student is often given messages like: *your struggles are an embarrassment, so let's agree that we will not talk about the fact that you are in ninth grade and can barely read or write or add. Here's your algebra worksheet. Pretend to do it.*

We imagine we are somehow doing these students at both ends of the spectrum a favour, making them fit in, preparing them for the real world (whatever exactly that is), sparing them the pain of being different from a hypothetical "typical" peer.

There are two main problems with this, though. The first and most obvious one is that humiliated, self-conscious, anxious children do not learn well. Overwhelming and unpleasant emotions shut down the kind of precise, creative, and concentrated thinking that is a crucial part of solving problems. And however cheerfully we might hand a high school level algebra assignment to a teen who can't add fractions, when he sees he can't understand it and is doomed to either copy someone else's work or get another failing grade, he'll feel inept and uneasy.

The second problem is more subtle. One of the deepest yearnings of most people, children and adults alike, is to be truly seen and accepted for who we are. Whatever our dreams and hopes for the future might be, and whatever mistakes we might have made in the past, we long for someone to convey: *I see you just as you are right now and I am here for you.* When we treat a child as if his needs are invisible and make it clear that those needs will not be met, we are really saying to the child: *you are invisible; your confusion and worry are invisible; your boredom and restlessness are invisible. I don't see you.*

This alienates children from themselves. They experience a painful divide between their real experience in the classroom and the experience they are pretending to have, or which the school is pretending they are having. Eventually, they stop asking for help when they're confused or requesting harder work when they need it.

What is the remedy for this?

We need to create a classroom environment in which it is perfectly acceptable to be working at any level. The classroom should have crystal clear behavioral expectations and rules and these should be strictly enforced. Everyone should be focused on learning; no one should be distracting anyone else, cheating, or wasting time. The standard for behavior should be very high — but with that in place, everyone should be completely free to work on whatever math will best serve her mathematical development. We need to switch the focus of the room from uniformity ("We will all work on concept 4.67 today") mixed with competition and comparisons ("Who got an A? Who failed?") to a focus on deep conceptual understanding and the joy that comes with it, individual progress, and group cohesiveness.

Group cohesiveness does not entail everyone always working on the same thing but rather everyone learning so intensely that the energy and spirit of the group moves everyone forward; the children should be focused on solving problems, making breakthroughs, helping others in truly effective ways, asking for help when they need it, and developing the skills that will enable them to progress efficiently. They should not be focused on feeling superior (or inferior) to others, looking down on others, hiding their confusion, or seeking relief from boredom by annoying others.

The teacher needs to model this attitude by providing the right level of work for every child in the room without conveying any sense of disappointment or exasperation with low or high achievers, and reinforce this inclusiveness by encouraging hard work, progress, understanding, insight, and helpfulness. A child who is four years behind but working hard should be treated with exactly the same level of mathematical respect and given just as much encouragement and positive feedback as a child who is right on grade level, as should a child who is a few years ahead.

There should be an overarching goal during a child's years in school: for the child to master at least all the important concepts contained in the K-12 curriculum and become a superb problem solver. On any given day, though, the immediate focus for each child should be on her mastering whatever math topics will best serve her development and growth.

a six-year-old solving equations using Cuisenaire rods

The teacher should openly praise children for asking for help, for persistence, and for helping others. Suppose, in a fourth-grade class which includes students whose levels range from first grade to ninth, one of the children masters borrowing. She does this by working hard, asking for help, and practicing. This child should be encouraged and praised just as much as a child who has mastered dividing fractions. If the lagging child asks for help, the teacher should show just as much enthusiasm for borrowing as she would for a more advanced topic. Why? Because the classroom focus should be on hard work and growth, not on comparing the children to each other and to an arbitrary list of ever-shifting, politically-driven grade-level math standards.

Imagine if the lagging child works extremely hard, masters borrowing, and is told she is failing math and is three years behind and is doing worse than most of the class. Will this motivate her to keep making progress? Almost certainly not. Instead, she will likely feel her efforts are pointless. This leads to a state of powerlessness and panic which is the worst possible state to be in when trying to learn math. Children should be encouraged to sink deeply into whatever topic they need to be working on and to happily and comfortably make sense of this topic rather than having their concentration frayed by pressure to perform at a level they simply are not at yet. Singular focus is a critical part of success in math. We want to help children develop this ability to focus, whatever their level of math proficiency.

We should champion each child's potential and never assume that a child who has fallen behind will stay behind, or that a child whose thinking is scattered and chaotic will stay that way — but we can never really help a child without meeting her where she actually is.

At the same time as children are allowed to work at their real level, the teacher should maintain clear records of exactly which K-12 concepts every child has mastered and which she has not. This precise record keeping needs to go along with the more flexible and fluid practice of encouraging everyone to work at her own level and pace. Naturally, these records should not be shared with the class or ever used to publicly humiliate a child. A child's math mastery record should be added to regularly and passed on to the next year's teacher so the big picture is always clear.

10

ASSESSMENT AS A MEANS OF HELPING CHILDREN

If we are to provide every child in a classroom with the appropriate level of math, we need a way of determining what this level is. An assessment is needed — but not the kind of assessment that is currently in place. The standardized testing which takes place in public schools every spring is enormously time-consuming and expensive. In some schools, teachers spend months preparing their students for these tests regardless of whether the test content is beyond the children's level or far below it.

Being able to perform well on exams is an invaluable skill, but one which should be taught directly (not by trial and error) in a far more targeted and efficient manner when it is developmentally appropriate (middle and high school). As it is now, teachers are devoting weeks or months trying to get children as young as seven to perform on poorly-worded tests which do not necessarily measure useful skills and which must be taken on computers which frequently malfunction. The whole enterprise is stressful for teachers who feel they must teach concepts they know will be on the test, regardless of whether these concepts seem appropriate for or accessible to their particular students.

How, exactly, does all this testing benefit the children who take the tests?

~

Let's examine the cases of two nine-year-olds, Tamisha and Anthony, who, like millions of other children, participate in this testing. In April of fourth grade, they spend a total of twelve hours, spread out over several days, taking these tests. Much of their school year has been geared toward meeting the fourth grade standards and the mastery of these standards is said to be accurately measured by these tests.

At the end of the summer following fourth grade, months after the children took the tests, Tamisha and Anthony's parents receive letters in the mail showing how their children did relative to other children.

Tamisha's parents are pleased to see that Tamisha has scored in the 83rd percentile in math (which puzzles them a little as she often exploded in frustration while doing her homework, claiming it made no sense), but concerned that her reading skills are only in the 48th percentile. Anthony's mother is horrified to see Anthony has scored in the 15th percentile in math which makes his 35th percentile score in reading skills seem almost cheering.

No one contacts the parents about the scores. Anthony's mother wonders if his low scores mean he has failed fourth grade. She doesn't know whether to tell Anthony that he may need to repeat his grade, or whom to contact. She tries calling Anthony's school but finds it closed for the summer. Having stood over Anthony all last year making sure he did his homework, she is mystified by why he did so exceptionally badly. Was it his fault? Was it her fault? Was it his teacher's fault? Is something wrong with Anthony? Should she be doing something about it? Is it possible he knew more of the material than his score suggests but did not understand how to enter his answers properly into the computer that was assigned to him? His mother can't see either the test questions or his answers so she has no way of knowing.

She sits him down to talk about it and his eyes fill with tears. "I'll try harder next year," he promises. He looks worried and troubled by the news that he did not do well and goes quietly off to his room after their conversation instead of returning to play with his older brother who did much better on the tests than Anthony despite being far more resistant to doing his homework and having worse grades in school.

When the new school year starts at the end of August, no one at the school says a word about Anthony's dreadfully low math test scores. Anthony is welcomed into fifth grade. His mother is relieved. Maybe everything will be fine after all. She is also puzzled. Why wasn't Anthony held back? She does not want to raise the issue since Anthony, whose favourite part of school is recess, is excited to be starting 5th grade with all his friends.

By late September, Anthony is failing math. When his mother goes to Back to School Night and asks the teacher what she can do to help Anthony, the teacher offers no specifics. "He tries hard," the teacher says and adds, "Be sure he does his homework every night."

His mother already devotes an hour a night to urging Anthony to plug away at the homework. Though his mother has a good understanding of all the fifth-grade topics and did well in math as a child, even she can't earn a good grade in the class. Knowing she is doing the wrong thing but unable to put Anthony through another hour of misery one night when he has a sore throat and looks exhausted, she tucks him into bed and picks up a pencil and in deliberately messy ten-year-old boy handwriting puts in all the right answers on the worksheet. This comes back with a C-. "Answer is correct but proper explanation is missing," and "Use the method we learned in class!" is scribbled in red ink liberally over the page.

Anthony's mother knows Anthony is falling further and further behind, and so does Anthony — his F's and D's make this quite clear — but neither of them knows how to fix it. Anthony's teacher also knows something is wrong. Anthony keeps struggling and has come to dread math class. He hates being called on. He hates getting tests back and hides them in his backpack before other kids can see them and throws them into a garbage can on the way home from school. He remembers how worried his mother looked when she sat him down in the summer and he doesn't want to see that look on her face again. His father disappeared four years ago and he worries too that his father may return and learn that Anthony is terrible at math.

The assessment which Anthony took months earlier did not provide anyone in the situation with any useful information. It did, however, have one direct and powerful effect. In combination with the low scores of hundreds of other children at Anthony's school, it helps to keep real estate values in Anthony's area of town relatively low and drives up the value of homes in the neighboring city with its starkly contrasting high test scores. Prospective buyers can go online and see the test scores of the schools in neighboring districts. On Anthony's street, a 2 bedroom house might sell for $600,000. A mile away, in a different school district, a similar-sized house in the same condition might sell for $1.2 million.

The complex, time-consuming, and expensive testing process and the creation of district data did not serve Anthony, who devoted so many hours to the testing process, in any way.

What is needed is much shorter and more frequent assessing and record keeping— not hours and hours of testing in a huge burst — for the sole purpose of enabling Anthony's teacher to provide him with the level of math and the instruction he needs and helping his teacher communicate with his mother about very specific ways she can help him. A twenty-minute test would reveal plenty. Even a ten-minute test would be of great help.

In Anthony's case, a simple short assessment would reveal gaps in his understanding of place value, borrowing when subtracting numbers like 2001 - 99, fraction comparisons, and factoring. Had his actual math progress been kept track of since he started school — in the form of a frequently updated chart showing what topics he had mastered — his teacher would be able to glance at this, combine this information with gaps in Anthony understanding revealed by a recent quick quiz, and guide Anthony on what to work on next.

If Anthony were given direct instruction in these areas at the right pace for him, he would be able to move ahead in math instead of falling further and further behind.

At the start of every school year, the teacher should assess the mathematical level of every student in the class. The assessment questions should be presented as clearly as possible so that the child's mathematical skills, rather than English language skills or reading comprehension skills, are isolated. The questions should be aimed at discovering if the child has failed to master critical concepts from earlier grades, is right on track, or is able to solve problems from higher grade levels.

The children should be allowed to answer the questions in the most straightforward manner possible to minimize the chances of inaccurately measuring the child's skills. One practical version would be a paper and pencil test in which the students solve the problems and put the answers directly on the test page rather than filling in a set of numbered bubbles on another page. A second version would be a computerized test in which the students type in or click on a numerical answer. Khan Academy is ideal for this.

The children should be told in advance that it is not an ordinary test and the point of this assessment is to help the teacher teach them better; they may find some questions very easy and others too hard to answer, and this is perfectly fine. It should be explained that they will not get a grade or score from this assessment and the only possible consequence of getting a question wrong will be the teacher later making sure they learn whatever it was they were confused about.

The results of this assessment should be used by the teacher to start out everyone in the class at an appropriate level of instruction. The results of the assessment— obviously — should not be shared with the whole class. Nor should the results be used to increase or decrease the teacher's job security or salary, or the funding for the school, or real estate values. There should be one and only one purpose to the test: to help the children who take the test.

Further short, simple assessments should be offered very frequently throughout the school year in order to tailor each child's curriculum to his level of understanding.

Far more useful than a set of annual standardized testing scores for each child (which vary enormously depending on what kind of testing is in fashion and might show the child to be at the "advanced" level in math in third grade and "below basic" the following year) would be a single regularly updated chart which is maintained throughout the child's education and which shows which K-12 concepts the child has mastered so far and which concepts remain to be mastered.

The new teacher could look at this before meeting her new class and have a clear understanding of the range of levels she needs to prepare for. If her incoming fourth-grade class was, by chance, all at about the same level, she could plan to teach many more topics to the whole group. If she looked at the data on her students and saw that some of her class had yet to master kindergarten level skills and some were at a tenth-grade level, she would know that any topics she presented to the whole class would have to be very carefully chosen to engage this wide range.

Elaborate standardized math testing of young children does not further the primary goal of getting children to love math and understand it deeply. It diverts resources away from learning. It drives the curriculum in ways that interfere with learning. It infuses math class with anxiety and stress, both for the teacher and for the children. It breaks the natural flow of learning. Though this is not its intent, it shifts the focus away from meeting the immediate needs of the children to a vaguer and more distant goal.

Even if the children are told, "Don't worry about these days of testing … it won't show up on your report card and it's really just a way of measuring the school, not you," this will not protect the children from the insidious way this testing affects their entire school year. Their teacher is well aware that come spring, her students will be tested — in ways that may be mind-bogglingly confusing — on a very large and specific set of skills, and not just on the skills themselves but on how the children are judged (not necessarily accurately) to be thinking about the skills.

Instead of placing our faith in these tests, we should be placing our faith in teachers. When a teacher is given a class of children for a year, she should be entrusted with doing everything in her power to instill a deep love and understanding of math in every one of her students and she should be offered support, training (if wanted), resources, and materials to meet each child exactly where she is and serve each child so that by the end of the school year every member of the class has grown mathematically to the very top of her potential.

We should hold teachers accountable — but not for trying to get a random group of thirty children to perform well on a standardized test. Instead, we should be holding them accountable for making math enjoyable and interesting and maximizing growth in all their students. We should also hold them accountable for keeping a clear and accurate record of exactly what mathematical topics each student has demonstrated mastery of during the school year so that this record can be shared with the child's parents and next year's teacher, as well as the child herself if the teacher thinks this would be helpful.

If a teacher is able to move an eleven-year-old from a first grade level in math to the fourth grade level in a single year, the teacher (and the student) have done a magnificent job — yet this would show up as a failure for both on a standardized test. Likewise, if a teacher, by trying to comply with the standards, has stultified an eleven-year-old who began the year at ninth-grade level but lost many of these skills through lack of use and glazed boredom over the course of the year, this student's standardized test scores might show up as a wonderful success for both the teacher and the student when nothing could be further from the truth.

Individual teachers do not have the power to reject the testing their district has agreed to. This rejection of the kind of testing which undermines learning needs to come from a higher level. Teachers do, however, have the power to frequently and non-stress-fully assess their students so they can make sure every one of their students is working on the appropriate level of math. One would very much hope that a teacher would not be disciplined for focusing on maximizing mathematical growth and joy rather than standardized test scores.

11

ENLISTING CHILDREN'S HELP IN THE ASSESSMENT PROCESS

As well as offering frequent low-stress assessments to help determine what material will best serve each child, there is an important way we can teach children to actively participate in figuring out what they need to learn next.

The most common reason for a child being unable to solve a math problem is that she lacks the foundational skills to solve it. This is a very different issue from having the necessary skills to solve a tricky problem and needing to look at it from different angles, perhaps try different approaches, and persist until one is successful. The latter process leads the child to become a more skilled and confident problem-solver. But what if the child simply does not have the background to solve the problem?

Consider this math problem: *Prove that a bounded holomorphic function on the complex plane is constant.*

Most readers will not be able to solve this problem even if they set everything aside and work on it for ten hours straight. This is because they likely will not know what a bounded holomorphic function is, and perhaps also will not know what the complex plane is, and if they look these terms up, they won't be much further ahead.

Now consider this problem: Cut out the seven shapes and arrange them into a square.

Some readers may instantly recognize that these shapes are the pieces of a tangram and remember how they form a square and cut them out and arrange them within a minute or so. Other readers may be unfamiliar with tangrams and find that once they cut the pieces out, it is not obvious how to place them into a square. Every reader, though, will be able to arrange them into a square by persisting.

Most people, upon reading each of the two problems above, will know right away that the first problem is out of their range (unless they happen to have studied Complex Analysis) and that the second problem, assuming it has a solution, is completely manageable. These problems represent extremes, though, and between them is a grey area where one can't tell at a quick glance if one has the adequate skills and knowledge to solve the problem at hand.

Consider this third problem: *Find the area of a triangle with sides 3, 4, and 6.*

You may not instantly know whether you have the necessary math background to solve this. The problem sounds easy enough. A triangle is a very simple shape, and the numbers 3, 4, and 6 are small and manageable. Playing with it for a bit, though, you might arrive at the conclusion that the triangle is not a right triangle so while the base might be known, the height is not. This leads to the question: how can one find the area of a triangle if one can't use the familiar formula Area = 1/2 base x perpendicular height? This is the single piece of information many readers might lack, and identifying this gap in knowledge is critical to solving the problem (for most people). For a problem of this level of complexity, if you know exactly what you don't know, it is usually a matter of learning that specific thing (in this case, Heron's Formula) in order to succeed.

~

The critical first step in solving a math problem

We want children to develop the practice of asking themselves, before spending a long time on a problem whose solution does not seem obvious, **"Do I have the knowledge and skills to solve this problem?"** and then making that determination.

Teachers tend to gloss over this critical first step in problem-solving and convey to students that if they just keep trying, they will be able to complete the assignment at hand. This often leads children to make the same assumption. While there are math problems for which nothing but persistence is required (like the tangram problem above), this is not true of most problems.

Most math problems require a precise set of skills and very specific background knowledge. Millions of hours are wasted in math classes — particularly classes like algebra — because children are staring at problems they cannot solve, not because they don't want to solve them or don't care about math, but because they lack the skills to tackle the problem.

Children should be taught that the very first step in solving a problem they feel puzzled by is to ask themselves, **"Is this a matter of persisting, or do I need to learn something before I can solve this problem?"** Teaching children to make this distinction will empower them and help them determine what they need to master next.

We want children to study the problem carefully and, instead of entering an unproductive state of anxiety or overwhelm or boredom, pin down as precisely as possible what skill or information they are lacking.

We want their thoughts to go something like, "I can't solve this problem because I don't know how to divide," or, "I'm completely stuck because I don't know how to add fractions and I see that I am going to need to learn that in order to do this problem" or, "I don't know how to solve this because I don't know what cotangent means," rather than, "I have no clue how to do this! This class is so awful! I hate math so much. When is the bell going to finally ring?"

We want children to take charge of their learning by figuring out the most urgently needed skill they must learn next. We want them to start advocating for themselves and pressing to learn the skills they need. It is much better to have a fourteen-year-old say, "I never understood how to add fractions. Will you show me how?" or, "I never really got exponents. Will you teach me how they work?" than to have that child sit for weeks in algebra class, failing and falling further and further behind. Children are most highly motivated to learn a skill when they feel an urgent need for it.

This is so important that I would urge teachers to give their students green pencils and ask the children to circle or underline every word they don't know the meaning of and every concept in a problem that they are confused by whenever they get stuck. I suggest green because it will stand out. Red is not ideal because many children associate it with getting things wrong. We want children to link identifying missing skills or information with learning and moving ahead rather than with making mistakes or failing.

For example, if a child is told to factor a set of quadratic equations and she has no idea how to proceed (a very common occurrence), rather than staring at the problem feeling incompetent and out of her depth, she should be allowed to pick up her green pencil and circle the words factor and quadratic if these are the two terms she is perplexed by. There is no point in her sitting in front of the problems hoping the knowledge of these things will suddenly come. It definitely won't. The one thing that is almost guaranteed to come is a feeling of shame mixed with helplessness.

What is probably needed in this particular case is for the child to back up to much simpler equations, solve lots of those, learn what the word factor means and factor very simple expressions and then harder ones, learn what a quadratic equation is and how to distinguish one from a linear equation, and then learn to factor the simplest of quadratics. This may sound like a long detour (and it will take time), but is it the only way the child will be able to move ahead with understanding.

Rather than being shamed or dismissed for admitting significant gaps in knowledge, children should be highly praised for this and helped. The self-awareness and bravery involved in admitting a gap is a crucial part of the shift from struggling math student to competent one. It is never too late to learn foundation skills. Without them, however, failure is almost guaranteed.

In encouraging children to play an active role in determining what they need to learn next in order to solve the problems at hand and what gaps they need to fill in their backgrounds in order to progress, we get an ongoing, finely-tuned and accurate method of assessing their level of mastery and their progress: children declaring, “I haven’t learned how to add decimals yet and I need to!” or, “I don’t really understand how to tell if something is a function,” or, “I don’t know how a negative exponent works.” Children’s own admissions of confusion and requests for direct instruction and clarity on specific topics, as they are working on appropriate-level problems, have much more practical value than a set of annual standardized tests.

To get a better feel for what we want students to learn to do, read each of the following questions carefully and ask yourself, “Do I have the knowledge and skills to solve this problem?” If you come to a problem you don’t think you would be able to solve, try to identify the terms or procedures you do not know. This is exactly how children should be taught to read problems.

- Find the volume of a cylinder with radius 2.5 and height 15. Find the dimensions of a cone which has the same volume.
- What is the product of the ninth and tenth terms of the sequence -4, 1, 6, 11, …?
- Solve the following system of 2 equations in 2 unknowns: $6x + 4y = 22$, $5x + 2y = 10$
- If a 13-foot ladder is leaning against a wall and touches the wall 12 feet above the ground, how far is the base of the ladder from the wall?
- Find the area bounded by $y = x^2$ and $y = 2x$.

12

CONTINUOUS FEEDBACK WHILE TEACHING

In a typical math class, the teacher stands at the board and explains a new topic or goes over homework or reviews an old topic. A handful of students might get called on, and these will often be the ones who are raising their hands. Occasionally the teacher might call on a daydreamer to embarrass or jolt him into paying attention. At the end of the explanation, the teacher might ask if the class understands and if anyone has any questions.

What is so terribly wrong with this very common and well-intended approach?

The teacher has no idea, while teaching, if most of the students are understanding. Half the class could be tuned out and a further quarter could be listening but not understanding at the level that will allow them to solve similar problems on their own, and the teacher will not be aware of this.

Questions like, "Does everyone get it?" or, "Any questions?" rarely elicit admissions of confusion from the most perplexed students. The students who are most likely to ask a question are those who understand almost all the material but are puzzled by one or two small points, and who have the greatest chance of being able to resolve their confusion on their own. Those who are deeply confused and very unlikely to be able to solve the problems later typically feel some degree of embarrassment about this (or are too bored to bother asking for help) and will not respond to the question, "Do you understand?" As for the daydreamer, after the initial jolt of being asked a question he does not know the answer to in front of his peers wears off, he will most likely slide back into daydreaming. A flash of embarrassment is rarely an effective way to engage a student in math as it does not address any of the reasons he was tuned out in the first place.

Long ago, this style of teaching math became the norm. Most of us take it for granted — even though it is shockingly inefficient.

What is actually needed is for the teacher, while presenting concepts at the board, to elicit a steady stream of accurate feedback from the students which lets her know, moment to moment, who is understanding, how much they are understanding, who is confused and what precisely is confusing them, and who is not paying attention even though they might be quietly facing the board.

This feedback will enable the teacher to tailor the lesson to these particular students and their immediate needs. If half the class is not paying attention, this needs to be responded to instantly by the teacher — not a day or two later when homework is handed in which reveals the children did not absorb the concept. If five children don't know what the word denominator means when the teacher is using the term, this needs to be attended to in that very moment — not six months later when standardized testing exposes this gap in knowledge.

We tend to expect moment to moment responsiveness in one-on-one conversations or individual tutoring sessions yet dismiss it as a possibility in large (or even small) group situations.

When I was twenty-two and attending a graduate program in gifted math education at the University of Washington, I chanced to learn of a program based in Berkeley which took a radically different approach to student feedback. The organization which taught this feedback method was called Project SEED and was started in 1963 by a man called William Johntz.

William Johntz was a math teacher at Berkeley High at that time. He was dismayed and horrified that other members of the math department boasted that they had never had a black student in algebra. This appalling racist claim was intended to convey that the math department kept their standards high — too high for black students to enter an algebra class, let alone pass one. The black students were grouped in remedial math classes.

This kind of boasting was chilling to Mr. Johntz and played a major role in his decision to devote the rest of his life to encouraging black students to excel in algebra. Rather than vying with other teachers to teach the classes of high achievers, he requested only remedial classes — but instead of focusing on remediation, he taught his students algebra. His previously failing students did learn algebra but as he worked with them, it struck him that the most efficient and practical time to get students to excel in math was not during their high school years when they were beset by the challenges of adolescence and had already developed a firm conviction that they were bad at math. He did not give up on his teenaged students but he decided to seek out their younger brothers and sisters. Each day he would walk across Martin Luther King Junior Way (then called Grove Street) to Washington Elementary at lunchtime and during his free period to teach algebra.

He taught the children not by lecturing or giving them rules to memorize but by asking them questions, sometimes as many as a hundred to a hundred and fifty questions in a class period. The questions were designed to lead the children to think deeply and conceptually about the math they were studying. The children were quite startled to learn that they were able to understand concepts that many teenagers have trouble with and they began to see themselves as far more intelligent and capable than they had previously assumed. They became so enthusiastic that when Mr. Johntz would pose a question, the whole class would try to answer and chaos would quickly ensue.

William Johntz teaching in the early days of Project SEED

In his determination to maintain order in the face of this eagerness and reach every single child in his classes, William Johntz taught the class a set of arm and finger signals with which they could silently convey responses throughout the lesson. This combination, of being asked questions throughout the lesson and invited to respond continually, transformed the learning experience for the children. Before long, mathematicians and scientists from UC Berkeley heard that William Johntz was teaching high school topics to young children and came and learned the method from him and his project grew from there.

~

It was 1982 when I first heard of this. It sounded so much more promising than the teaching methods I was being taught in the graduate program I was taking. After a long phone conversation with William Johntz, I decided to move to Berkeley and learn the method.

The requirement at that time for teaching in Project SEED was a degree or two in math or science or engineering, and a deep desire to share one's knowledge and love of math with young children from low-performing schools in impoverished areas. One began by watching lots of Project SEED classes, taking notes on what was working and why it was working, and then discussing the class in detail afterwards with the mathematician who had just taught it.

The central premise of Project SEED was that the way to turn a struggling, demoralized, low-achieving child into a high achiever was not by telling him he could do anything (in the spirit of a pep rally), and not by lowering standards and passing him. Rather, the transformation would require that the child have a direct, powerful, prolonged and unforgettable experience of academic success in a challenging subject (mathematics) which would convince the child, beyond a shadow of a doubt, that he was bright and capable.

~

I arrived in September, a beautiful golden month in the Bay Area, moved into a corner room in a home high up in the Berkeley Hills with a family who became my best friends, and began driving to schools in the little red Toyota my mother had kindly passed on to me. Quite fearlessly, I would drive into the depths of East Oakland, glancing down now and then at a map spread out on the seat beside me, and find whatever school I knew had a Project SEED class slated to take place at that hour. The Project SEED teachers would go into classrooms and teach an entire class during their math period while the regular classroom teacher observed.

I was amazed and captivated. A few months earlier I had grown so disenchanted with the gifted math education program I was enrolled in that I had decided I would not become a math teacher after all and would instead apply to medical school.

After watching a few discovery-style algebra classes in elementary classrooms in East Oakland, my longing to teach math returned. The mathematician would walk to the front of the room and within seconds have the entire class spellbound, actively participating, and bursting with enthusiasm. It was utterly unlike the math classes I'd endured during my years in public schools. During a fifty-minute period, the children were intensely focused on the unfolding Socratic dialogue. Their feedback was elicited every few seconds. Most of the time only one person was allowed to talk at a time — yet over and over the children would wave their hands to show they agreed, they disagreed, they thought the answer was 6, or 8, they were confused, or they had a question. I had never seen anything remotely like this level of engagement in a classroom, ever.

The students in the room were generally low achieving children, many of them already two or three years behind academically even though they were only in elementary school, yet they did not appear to be low achievers; they looked like highly motivated scholars, madly waving their hands to answer a question or simply answering silently by showing a number or symbol with their fingers. Whenever they disagreed with anything the teacher or another student was saying, they would wildly scissor their arms and hope to be called on to explain what Mr. Johntz referred to as their "intellectual protest." They were not learning arithmetic in these classes but rather aspects of algebra that did not rely on skills they had missed.

I watched, entranced, and could hardly wait to get up in front of a class myself. When I did — and luckily I did not have to wait long — I found that an unexpected thing happened. The orchestration of the class, the tuning into thirty different minds, the eliciting of all their feedback, and the careful tailoring of my next question to precisely this feedback and not some preconceived lesson plan, lifted me out of myself into a state of joy I'd never experienced before.

I learned many things during my years of teaching in Project SEED — indeed it was the richest learning experience of my life — but the single most valuable thing I learned was how to engage an entire class and elicit a stream of continuous feedback from the class. Once one has taught in this way, it is impossible ever to go back to talking "at" a group and ignoring the fact that many of them may be confused or tuned out. The original arm signals I learned were:

- **"I agree."** (Pumping arms.)
- **"I disagree."** (Scissoring arms.)
- **"I partly agree and partly disagree."** (One arm pumping and the other doing a sideways motion.)
- **"I don't know."** (Hands held palms up.)

In addition to these arm signals, students are asked to use their fingers (or arms) to show:

- **numbers**
- **operations** (addition, subtraction, multiplication, division)
- **directions**
- **shapes**
- **brackets**

A couple of years before I saw my first Project SEED class, I had taught algebra at a college in Canada. I had done my best to make the material accessible to my students, but I felt separate from my students, isolated at the front of the room, scanning as I taught to see if the expressions of my thirty students indicated that I was making sense to them or not. I could not tell whether some of them were bored or exhausted, nor could I distinguish between an expression of comprehension and one of polite diligence masking confusion. No matter how carefully I studied their faces, I never felt I had an accurate enough sense of what was going on in their heads. Instinctively I felt it was best to ask questions instead of lecturing without pause, but when I asked a question, one person would answer and I would have no idea what the other twenty-nine people were thinking.

When I began using the group discovery method I could ask a question like, "What is fifteen minus twenty?" and in response to this, I might see most of the class showing negative five with their fingers, two children holding up positive five, thee people showing, "I don't know," and two children not showing any response. This would give me a quick reading that most children were understanding, a few weren't and needed additional help, and two children needed to be drawn in more.

Students eagerly hold up seven on their fingers when their ten-year-old teacher asks them to show the exponent of the answer to a problem he has posed.

Over the next few years, I added a number of additional arm signals to further refine this process. Each of these signals represented a response that often came up and would help children express themselves and help me get a more accurate sense of what they were thinking.

The first signal I added was called "stolen answer." I noticed that one of the most frustrating aspects of the class to the children involved their frantically waving their hands to be called on to explain something, only to have another child called on first. The children who had not been called on would bring their hands down swiftly in disappointment, sometimes slamming the desktops with an open palm.

This sound was disruptive, but I realized its main purpose was not to annoy but to convey, "I wanted to say that! *I* had that explanation ready!" I told the students that instead of slamming the desks, they could use the stolen answer signal which meant, "That person just gave the answer that *I* had already thought of." The signal involved grabbing handfuls of air and could be done very vigorously. After calling on one child (if the answer could not be shown easily on fingers), I could swiftly acknowledge the children doing the stolen answer signal by saying, "I see Jessica and Joey and Deshaun all had the answer ready too. Excellent."

The desk slamming stopped because the children preferred the slightly humorous quality of the stolen answer signal, the specificity of what it meant, and the acknowledgement they got when they did it.

The process of understanding a challenging new math idea often has a number of stages: bafflement, the beginning of understanding, a deepening of this understanding, and then an exhilarating burst of pure clarity.

"Stop! I have a question."

The idea of having these stages demonstrated with the hands at the same time as the process was unfolding in the mind appealed to both me and the children so together we developed five more arm signals:

- **"Stop! I'm confused!"** (One hand held in a stop sign, the other held palm up, eyebrows raised.)
- **"Confusion breaker."** (Meaning, "I can clear up the confusion," and shown with a silent snapping forward of the arms as if to break a thin sheet of ice.)
- **"I'm starting to understand."** (One lightbulb, formed with thumb and forefinger, held over the head.)

- **"I really understand."** (Two lightbulbs held over the head.)
- **"I've had a total breakthrough!"** (Two bouncing lightbulbs held over the head.)

These became the children's favourite signals. The "stop, I'm confused" signal gave them tremendous power. Instead of the teacher barreling on at a pre-set pace that did not reflect what was actually going on in the students' minds, any student could grind this to a halt at any second, simply by thrusting forward a stop sign and holding up the other hand in an expression of uncertainty. A good deal of people's willingness to try new things has to do with a sense of control. Many children are much more willing to explore brand new and very complex ideas if they feel that can have a major role in determining the pace and even some of the content.

The confusion breaker signal helps to develop helpful and help-requesting relationships not just between the teacher and students but among the students themselves. When I introduced this signal, I noticed that the students remained far more focused when another child was needing extra help during a group discovery session. Ordinarily, this might be a time to tune out or daydream, but the appeal of breaking the confusion of another person was greater than the appeal of a daydream. The children listened carefully to see if the confusion involved an area they had grasped and began to plan in their heads how they would make the concept crystal clear.

The use of arm signals switches the focus of the group discovery session away from drawing distinctions between the high achieving students and the struggling ones, or the quick and the slow, to an enjoyment of very effective communication. The children's energy goes into perfecting and explaining a metaphor or a diagram to help another child rather than into feeling superior to the confused person. Likewise, the confused child, immediately upon confessing his confusion, realizes he is surrounded by a group of people who want to draw him into a deeper understanding, partly out of helpfulness, and partly because it is so much fun to do so.

~

Over time, we added these signals as well:

- **"I have a question."** (One arm and hand curved in a question mark, the other hand in a fist below. The bottom hand can alternate between being the dot at the bottom of the question mark and pointing to the person the child wants to question, or a circling motion indicating a desire to pose a question to the whole class.)
- **"Stop! I have a question."** (One hand up, the other pushed forward.) This combination of arm signals is more urgent that simply having a question and indicates the child must ask the question immediately in order to follow what is being said.
- **"I have a theory to propose."** (Arms forming a big "T".)
- **"Please repeat your last statement."** (Both hands making a gesture toward oneself.)
- **"Please turn up the volume."** (A twisting motion with one hand to indicate that one cannot hear what is being said.)
- **"I can't see the board."** (Flat hands moving back and forth over eyes.)
- **"Algebra applause."** (Vigorous silent clapping, with the palms not quite touching, to indicate an appreciation of someone else's great idea or insight or explanation.)
- **"I just changed my mind."** (Fingers of both hands touching temples, then shifting sideways as if a set of thoughts has just been moved out of the mind.)

Each of these signals serves to facilitate the learning process. Children are often filled with powerful emotions during a lively math discussion and the signals offer them a way to express these emotions passionately which only adds to the excitement and energy of the lesson. Without a way of physically expressing confusion or disagreement, many children will reach a point of frustration where they will either shout out disruptively or withdraw completely.

The "I can't see the board" and "turn up the volume" signals turned out to be surprisingly important. I realized that without these signals, children (and adults) will sit through entire classes in which there is too much glare on the board to see all the symbols, or in which they cannot hear properly. Though no child had ever raised a hand to say she could not see or hear, when I taught the children these signals they typically were used at least five to ten times during a lesson. The moment I stood in a place that blocked a child's view, the child would start signaling. Or, if a child were explaining an idea in too soft a voice, eight to ten children across the room would start doing the "turn up the volume" signal. The ability to control being able to see and hear well contributes to a sense of personal power and further removes children from passive or even helpless roles. The more powerful they feel, the more they are inclined to admit confusion and ask insightful questions, and the more deeply they will learn.

These children are controlling the pace of the algebra lesson by making it clear that they do not understand the last thing that was said and they want an explanation that makes more sense to them. The little boy's fleetingly knitted brow and the little girl's perplexed expression might have been missed — but their "Stop! I'm confused!" signals could not possibly go unnoticed. The lesson will not move on until both children are satisfied they completely understand the new concept.

Ongoing feedback is absolutely vital to the success of a math class. Without an unfolding exchange between the teacher and the entire class, most explanations at the board are a waste of time for most children in the room.

13

NO FEEDBACK VS CONTINUOUS FEEDBACK: A CONTRAST IN TEACHING STYLES

Here is an example of a teacher presenting a topic without asking for meaningful feedback:

Teacher: Today we're going to learn about exponents. Two to the fifth power is equal to two times two times two times two times two which is thirty-two. [Rapidly writes 2 x 2 x 2 x 2 x 2 = 32 on the board.] See? You take the base here [taps the 2] and raise it to the power of the exponent … in this case the five… which means you multiply two by itself five times. Everyone get that? Ten to the sixth power is a million because ten times itself six times is a million. [Quickly adds this example below the other example.] Make sense? Okay, now turn to page 104 and do all the odds while I correct last night's homework.

With this kind of teaching, even though the words are quite clear and the concept is not difficult, most of the children in the room will tune out the teacher's voice and not absorb the concept.

Here is an example of a teacher eliciting a continuous stream of feedback from the whole class while conveying the same concept:

The teacher writes 2^3 = on the board.

Teacher: We read this as, "Two to the third power equals." Now I want all of you to read it to me as I run my finger underneath it.

Class [exuberantly]: Two to the third power equals!

Teacher: Very good. Now I'm going to write another problem.

The teacher writes 2^4 = on the board.

Teacher: Raise your hand if you can read this problem? Jenny?

Jenny: Two to the fourth power equals.

Teacher: Excellent. Now, in 2^3, the two is called the base and the little three up here is called the exponent. [Teacher writes these two words at the side of the board.] I want the whole class to show me on your fingers, what is the base in 2^3?

Most people hold up two fingers.

Teacher: I see almost all of you recognize that the base is two. Aisha, how did you know two was the base?

Aisha: Because it's the bigger number under the little number.

Teacher: Yes, well put. Everyone, show me on your fingers, if two is the base in 2^4, what is the exponent?

Most children hold up four fingers.

Teacher: Good! Now let's look again at 2^3. This equals 2 x 2 x 2. [Teacher writes 2x2x2 after 2^3 = .] What does 2 x 2 x 2 equal?

Some students show six and some show eight.

Teacher: Lizzy, can you explain how you got that six?
Lizzy: I went two, four, six!

Vigorous silent disagreement breaks out around the room and some children show agreement.

Teacher: Laquisha, why are you disagreeing?

Laquisha: I got eight. Two times two is four and four times two is eight!

Lizzy and a few others signal "I changed my mind." Other children signal agreement with Laquisha.

Teacher: Lizzy, why did you change your mind?

Lizzy: I realised I was adding but it is really supposed to be timesing!

Teacher: Laquisha, you must have explained your answer very well because you got a few people to change their minds. And Lizzy, you're right. You need to multiply the twos. Who agrees that 2 x 2 x 2 is eight?

Lots of children signal agreement. The teacher writes in 8.

Teacher: Now for 2^4, do I start writing down twos or fours? Show me on your fingers.

The class holds up twos.

Teacher: Excellent! I see you all know it is two. Now I am going to start writing twos and I want you to stop me with a silent stop sign the moment I have enough.

With lightning speed, the teacher manages to write five twos on the board before the students jam forward their silent stop signs.

Teacher (with feigned satisfaction): There!

The class vigorously signals disagreement.

Teacher: Why are you all disagreeing? Hands up to explain.

A sea of hands shoots up.

Teacher: Danny, can you explain why you're disagreeing?

Danny: The power is four so you need four twos but you put five twos! Erase one of those twos!

Teacher: Everyone, show me if you agree or disagree with Danny.

The class signals agreement. The teacher erases a two and now has this on the board:
$2^4 = 2\ 2\ 2\ 2$

Teacher: What operation do I put between these twos? Show me with your arms.

The class shows crossed arms forming Xs.

Teacher: Very good. Amanda, what operation are you showing?

Amanda: Multiplication.

Teacher: Okay, now I want you all to calculate 2^4 in your heads. [Teacher writes two little lines for the two digit answer after 2 x 2 x 2 x 2 = ___ .] Show me the ones digit on your fingers. I see lots of sixes. [Writes 6 in the one's place.] Now show me the tens digit.

Good, I see almost the entire class is showing me a one. [Writes in the 1.]

The teacher writes 2^5 under 2^4.

Teacher: Did I just change my base or my exponent? Call it out!

Class: Your exponent!!

Teacher: Yes. Am I going to need more twos or fewer twos this time? Point up if I need more and down if I need fewer.

Lots of fingers point up.

Teacher: Very good. Now this time you need to be on your toes and stop me fast with a silent stop sign when I get the right number of twos.

The teacher begins rapidly writing twos but this time the class is watching so carefully with arms pulled back that the moment the fifth 2 is on the board arms shoot forward in silent stop signs.

Teacher: Great! You stopped me in time. Two to the fifth power. I assume that will be ten. [Quickly writes 10 in for the answer.]

This statement is met with exuberant disagreement signals and some laughter.

Teacher (pretending to be baffled): Sam, why are disagreeing with me? Two times five is ten, isn't it?

Sam: You're not supposed to add those twos! Laquisha explained this. You need to keep doubling with each two.

Teacher: Thank you! Yes, we are supposed to be multiplying. Everyone show me the ones digit of the answer.

Almost everyone holds up two fingers.

Teacher: I see lots of twos but I also see a few people did not answer. Is anyone puzzled about where that two came from?

Noah does the "I am confused" signal.

Teacher: I see Noah is bravely showing puzzlement. Admitting when you are puzzled is the best thing you can do in this class. Who can explain where that two came from? Maria? Can you come up to the board and show how to get it?

Maria bounds up to the board and takes the chalk.

Maria: You see, you start here [pointing the chalk to the first 2] and you multiply by this 2. What is two times two, Noah?

Noah: Four.

Maria: Good. Now you multiply by the next two. Four times two. What do you get?

Noah: Eight.

Maria: Now multiply your eight by this two.

Noah: Sixteen.

Maria: And now by the last two. Sixteen times two?

Noah: Thirty-two. Now I get it! {Big smile spreading on his face.]

Maria [looking delighted]: Good!

Teacher: Great job, you two. Excellent teaching, and excellent learning. Now just before you sit down Maria, can you ask the class if they agree with Noah's thirty-two?

Maria [relishing her teaching job]: Class, show me with your arm signals if you agree with Noah.

The class enthusiastically shows agreement and a few students do the "silent applause" signal. Maria hands the chalk back to the teacher and sits down.

The class continues on in this manner for a few more minutes and then the teacher gives everyone some exponent problems to solve at their desks and briskly circulates, offering help and encouragement wherever needed.

This second version in which the teacher involves all thirty of her students and gets direct feedback on their level of engagement, focus, and understanding certainly takes more time and more energy than making a few statements at the board but the investment of time and energy is well worth it because it results in so much more learning and joy.

14

IMAGINE YOURSELF INSIDE THE MIND OF THE STUDENT

If I had to pin down the single most important aspect of effective teaching, I would say that it is to imagine one is the child (or children) one is teaching.

Before I ask a question, I first put myself inside the mind of the child I am addressing and then try to formulate the best possible question to lead that child to clarity. If the child is frustrated, I try to imagine exactly what that frustration feels like and identify its causes, and my next words will be based on trying to free the child from that frustration so he can happily move ahead with learning.

If I see a child looking confused, I don't go back to the beginning of the concept and start again and rattle off a few statements. Instead, I try to identify precisely what is confusing the child and I address exactly that, not the concept in general. I do this not by resting in and demonstrating my own mastery of the topic (a *very* common practice in the teaching of math), but by switching my point of view to that of the child.

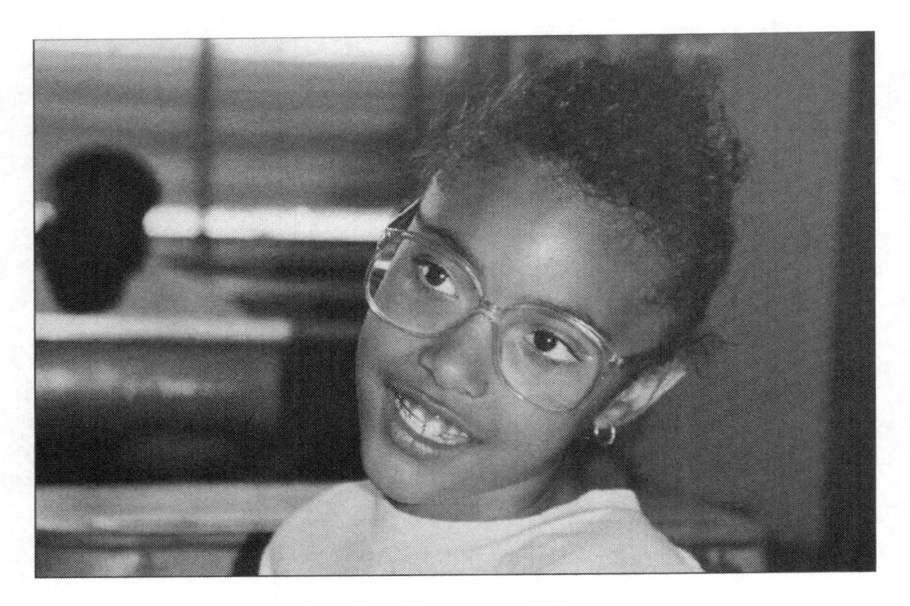

See each problem though the child's eyes.

This type of teaching is far more powerful and engages the child at a different level because he feels seen and heard and known, rather than talked at. He becomes a co-creator of the math rather than an object to be filled with facts or skills.

Hundreds of times I have had children say to me, "You made it so easy!" when I have said very little. When I was tutoring a thirteen-year-old girl named Emma who came once a week to my home, she would spread out her homework and study sheets and frustration and confusion and tell me that the teacher had gone on for an hour and she had not understood any of it.

I would glance at the topic — let's say it was solving pairs of inequalities — and I would try to picture what it was that had happened in her math class that had made it seem so nebulous and confusing, and I would imagine where the sticky points were in Emma's mind with all this, and then I would show her how to clear away all the unnecessary words and explanations and solve one problem of the same type with ease and clarity. This was what this particular child needed. She needed to see that the concept the teacher had covered the board with and talked about for an hour was really something she could grasp in a minute or two and then practice to get comfortable with.

Why did her well-meaning teacher go on for so long? I suspect it was because he was not getting any feedback from the children other than looks of boredom and non-comprehension. He knew something was not right and kept trying to fix this by saying more, and more, and more.

Unfortunately, the more a teacher says when things are not going well, the more the children recoil and tune out both the teacher's words and the equations on the board so the words become the "wah wah wah" of adults in Charlie Brown movies and the board-work becomes a solid, impenetrable mass. (This is true with older students as well.)

After I did my one clear example for Emma, I would say, "Now you do this one," and sitting beside her, I would watch. If she stumbled, I would already be imagining I was her doing the problem, and I would offer the tiny piece that she was missing. I would not explain the whole thing again, as if she had not heard anything I was saying. I would not offer a lecture on inequalities which would have put her back into the glazed state she had been in during her math class. Rather, I offered just the one small thing she needed, like handing someone who is removing a light switch plate a Philips screwdriver of just the right size instead of dumping out a toolbox at her feet.

Less is usually much, much more when it comes to math explanations — but that "less" needs to be based on exactly what is needed, and knowing what is needed involves tuning in to another person so deeply that you can sense and articulate what is confusing them. Saying too much tends to lead students to remove their attention from your voice and place it elsewhere.

When I am teaching a full-sized class, I use this same method. Each time I address an individual child, I put myself in her place, using the clues of her facial expression and words, her tone of voice and posture, and all that I have learned about her over recent days or months or years to imagine as precisely as I possibly can what exactly she needs in order to understand and take joy in the matter at hand.

15

FEEDBACK FOR STUDENTS WHILE THEY ARE SOLVING PROBLEMS

In addition to the teacher receiving ongoing feedback from the class while teaching, there is another kind of feedback that makes a huge difference in learning math: feedback for the student while he is working independently. Children learn much more efficiently when they are able to receive very frequent feedback on whether they are solving problems correctly.

In shaping a brain that is good at math, we want to maximize the amount of time the child is positively engaged in doing math and minimize the amount of time the child is unproductively lost, confused or tuned out. If a child spends hours, over a period of days, doing problems incorrectly, it would probably have been better not to have worked on the problems at all because bad habits and confused thinking are harder to overcome than simply a lack of knowledge or experience.

On the other hand, if a child is making mistakes and self-correcting or receiving ongoing feedback and getting back on track based on this feedback, this is extremely valuable. Making mistakes is a critical part of learning math, but these mistakes need to be recognized in a timely manner and corrected so the child ends up in a place of clarity and triumph, not in a bog of confusion and frustration.

What is the best way to provide children with ongoing feedback while they are working at their desks? Ideally, they would do some of their math each day on Khan Academy. This would enable them to check, every time they complete a problem, if they are on the right track. If they type in an answer and it turns out to be wrong, they are then prompted to rethink how they did it. They might be able to figure out their mistake on their own, or they might choose to click on a hint to see where they went wrong in their method, or they might decide to ask another student or the teacher for help. In all of these cases, this self-correcting process starts when they realize they have gotten the first problem in a series wrong — not several days after they have handed in a page of answers, a third of which might be wrong.

16

USING FEEDBACK TO CHANGE A CHILD'S SELF IMAGE

During my first year of teaching in the Bay Area, I encountered a worryingly thin eight-year-old named Jordan whom I have never forgotten. As was the custom in Project SEED, I arrived at the classroom just as math time was about to begin. The regular classroom teacher moved over to the side of the room, or to her desk, while I did the algebra teaching.

Jordan sat at the very back of the classroom, his desk separated from the formation of the other children's desks. His skin was dark but looked like it had been brushed with white chalk. He wore a miserable expression and was on permanent punishment, part of which involved not being allowed to play outside at recess. His mother, the classroom teacher explained to me, had just died and he and his seven brothers and sisters were about to be divided up and sent to relatives around the country.

The first time I called on him for an answer after he had bravely raised his hand, he struggled for a moment to pull his words together. While I was giving him time to articulate his thoughts, the regular teacher jumped into the pause and called across the room to me in a loud, clear voice, "Oh Jordan can't read, and Jordan can't write. He won't be able to do that problem." In effect, she was saying, "Lower your expectations for him. He has shown himself to be a hopeless case and this is something all of us here know about him, and you should too."

A few minutes later, when I circulated the room to check a problem I'd given the children to do in their algebra notebooks, I approached Jordan and saw that his face was wet with tears, streaking the chalkiness. I bent down to ask him what was the matter.

In a hoarse voice, he whispered to me, "She say I can't do them neg-tives."

His expression unsettled me. He looked into my eyes with desperation, as if he would not be able to bear it if he could not understand negative numbers. I knew I could not possibly afford to assume that because he could not read, write, or cooperate with his regular teacher, he would not be able to do algebra. I looked back into his penetrating eyes and told him that he would definitely be able to understand negative numbers.

I walked back to the board and continued to include him in the lesson. At first, his most reliable answer was to supply me with Greek letters when I needed them. "Could you give me a variable, Jordan?" I asked with utter confidence as I wrote an equation on the board. The little girls curled their lips skeptically and the little boys laughed quietly. Jordan had been made into a symbol of someone who could do nothing right; it would be impossible for him to give the new algebra teacher a variable.

"Alpha!" Jordan said, and it was as if the sun had broken through in his face. The face of every child in the room changed. Their expressions shifted from disdain to surprise to relief to happiness. I saw in that moment how their scorn for Jordan had been a way of protecting themselves from his extreme pain and failure. Their laughter over his shortcomings was not a real pleasure for them. His sudden success, though, had brought them happiness. They turned and smiled at him as if to welcome him into their circle of accomplished algebraists.

I continued to call on him and mention his signals ("I see Jordan is agreeing with that"), and draw him into the lesson in every way I could think of. Whenever I saw him holding up a correct answer on his fingers, I would make a point of mentioning it, sometimes linking his name to one of the class stars. "I see both Nia and Jordan think the answer is 5 …" I wanted to change not only his sense of himself as a valuable contributor but also the way the classroom teacher (who was watching every lesson) and his classmates viewed him.

Every time I spoke to him I addressed him as the highly intelligent child I was certain he was. I called on him for both hard and easy questions, and if he answered incorrectly, I never took this as proof that he was slow after all. He began to raise his hand more and more, offering answers with great enthusiasm.

A couple of weeks later, he shyly pressed into my hand a piece of paper which had been folded many times. I read it after class and was touched by its friendly message. Then I stopped short. The words blended into each other and were all spelled phonetically, but he had picked up a pen and written what he wanted to say to me on a piece of paper. This little boy who for several years had been a failing and almost invisible member of his math class had not only started to learn algebra but had suddenly started to write.

17

HOW I TAUGHT MY OWN CLASSES

When I taught my after-school classes in elementary and middle schools, I arrived at a balance between direct instruction and discovery. This is what a typical class was like:

I would get to the school a few minutes before the final bell rang announcing the end of the school day. One might think this would be a poor time to start a math class and that all the children would be tired or ready for a break but this never turned out to be a problem even though my classes were usually seventy-five to ninety minutes long.

I always brought with me my enormous canvas bag containing every mathematically-related hands-on puzzle I had ever found — a white polar bear that came apart into pieces, a set of tiny metal acrobats that could be arranged in pyramids on a magnetic base, tangrams, wooden rhombohedra that could be made into a larger rhombohedron, irregular foam shapes that could be locked together to make cubes, slider puzzles of dolphins and the earth, and dozens of other puzzles. For the first few minutes of class, every child in the room would work on their puzzle of choice and then come up for another from the bag or trade one with a classmate.

This segment of the class, which might have looked to a casual observer like nothing more than a bunch of children playing, was actually developing their spatial skills and their willingness to persist with something that was not easy or obvious. Most of these puzzles had a clear ending point, a moment of triumph when the puzzle had very obviously been solved. The chunks of polar bear — which at first looked so unlikely to fit together into a creature — would, in the end, make a perfectly smooth white bear. The six irregularly shaped pieces of foam would make a cube.

A huge part of mathematical competence involves persisting when the first attempts at solving a problem do not yield a solution or even an obvious way forward. These mathematical puzzles were a surprisingly easy way to develop this skill. Children absolutely love to solve puzzles. They love to play. They love to do things with their hands. They love problems that have a "Yes! I've done it!" conclusion. The children in my classes got startlingly good at the puzzles and even devised ways of making them still more challenging, such as putting the polar bear together with their eyes closed and a timer set.

In this way, the children were guided to solve puzzles over and over which required focus and persistence as well as reasoning and spatial skills, and which consistently led to success and a feeling of accomplishment.

The next part of the class always involved solving a deductive logic problem — sometimes as a group and sometimes individually. The children loved these problems so much that they demanded that I write a new one for every single class. (Some children stayed with me for seven or eight years so I had to write a great many of these problems.) As the children got more and more adept at solving them, I made them more and more complex. When I led the problem at the board, I guided the children through every stage, reading aloud each clue, asking them questions that would help them to put all the clues together, and showing them how to draw diagrams that would help keep track of information.

The deductive logic problems were another example of guiding children through each step of solving a challenging problem. The problems might contain as many as fifteen clues, and I sprinkled in mathematical terms which many of the children had not encountered before. A clue might read, "The thief's age was a palindromic prime," or, "All the suspects' ages were perfect squares." Because the children were so eager to solve the problem at hand (many of which were written as mysteries), they would focus intently on absorbing any new math terms or concepts which were embedded in the clues. Sometimes we would get to the end of the clues and the puzzle would not be solved. Some critical piece of information had escaped our notice during the first reading, and we would have to go back to the beginning and read more carefully.

Like the polar bear puzzle, there was a clear and satisfying endpoint. Children enjoy this clarity in math and it helps propel them on. They tend not to like unsatisfying and vague math assignments such as, "Record your thoughts about even and odd numbers," or, "Write a story about the number five" or, "Try to find a way to divide 35 into 78457. There are no wrong answers. What counts is your thought process so write that down." These three questions may sound very inclusive of everyone and very accepting of all answers — but children are not satisfied by this lack of rigour. Like most adults, they like to arrive somewhere, not just wander along taking little stabs at dividing but never quite learning a clear and efficient algorithm or ever getting the right answer. Rather than feeling included and accepted, they tend to feel restless and annoyed.

In order to motivate children to do math, the process needs to be satisfying. Children need to feel they are mastering skills and accomplishing something.

The next part of my math classes involved my giving everyone math problems on paper to solve. I prepared these before each class and always included a variety of different types of math. In a typical lesson, the children might solve twenty equations which required a knowledge of fractions and negatives, several number theory problems, an additional deductive logic problem, and a few geometry problems. I kept the main categories of math alive for them rather than focusing on algebra for a year and then switching to geometry and letting them forget a lot of the algebra they had learned. I built the concepts they had learned in recent weeks or months into their new problems.

Some children solved fifty problems over the course of the next hour and some solved far more than that. I never compared the children to each other but instead praised them for their efforts and accomplishments and for helping their classmates.

As the children worked, I moved around the room checking their work. The only grade I ever gave was an A+. When they got a problem or a set of similar problems right, I put an A+ on the top righthand corner. If they didn't get it right, I gave them a hint or asked a question to get them on the right track or taught them the technique they needed in order to solve the problem on their own. As soon as they succeeded and I rechecked their work, they got their A+. No F's or even B's were ever given. They either did it right or kept on trying. What is the point in getting a math problem half-right and then moving on to something else?

My goal was to teach them to think in precise and efficient and logical ways that enabled them to solve a huge variety of math problems. I was teaching them how and why to persist. Every bit of this involved their actively doing math, never sitting passively while I did math.

The questions I gave were varied in difficulty. Some could be solved in a second. Others might take a few minutes. Occasionally I gave problems that might take far longer than that.

A complicated question that takes intense focus and perhaps a few tries builds in the child's brain what I think of as the circuitry for success — provided the child either arrives at the solution entirely on her own or is guided toward the solution with hints and suggestions. In both cases (guided or unguided) the child does the work and arrives at a clear endpoint.

On the other hand, a complicated problem that the child either gives up on, gets wrong (and knows he got wrong but does not correct), or cheats on, leaves a lingering uncomfortable sense of "I never understood that ... I'd prefer to avoid that sort of thing in the future." Repeated experiences of this type — which are tremendously common in school — damage a child's willingness and ability to do math. Young children would probably be better off doing no formal math at all than having hundreds of experiences of failure and frustration in the early elementary years.

My classes typically lasted an hour and fifteen minutes and were held once a week. (I went to a different school each day of the week.) Many children told me that during that time, they learned much more math than they did during the entire rest of the week. In the summer I held classes which were four hours long (part of the time I devoted to creative writing, and I gave two breaks to run around and play).

On Saturdays, in the early 90's, I taught classes for nine to eleven-year-olds at U.C. Berkeley that lasted several hours. Half the time was devoted to mathematical exploration and the other half to science experiments. These classes, offered through the MESA Program, were specifically for minority children whose races were under-represented at the university. The goal of the classes was to allow the children to experience success in challenging math and science and get them to feel comfortable and at home on the U.C. Berkeley campus. In all these different settings, the children solved a remarkable number of problems because they were so motivated and focused.

18

MATHEMATICAL ELEGANCE

Children have a highly developed sense of when adults are being direct and straightforward with them. They know when they are being condescended to and when they are being given mindless busywork. They do not like being asked to do things in convoluted, awkward ways.

When mathematicians are solving problems, they do not try to come up with cumbersome, roundabout ways of arriving at solutions. Perhaps the highest praise in math is the word "elegant".

What is mathematical elegance? A mathematical proof is considered elegant if it is simple, direct, clear, and lucid. Praise is never heaped on mathematicians for taking three pages to explain what could have been said in three lines.

If we want children to love math, we need to unveil its beauty years before they have come to detest it. Elegance is a critical aspect of this beauty. It is essential that concepts and methods be taught in the most direct and simple way.

Any time a new concept or procedure is introduced, the teacher should constantly ask herself questions like:

- What is the simplest possible way to do this?

- How can I make this concept crystal clear using the fewest words?
- What is the most direct and retraceable path to the solution?
- What, precisely, is confusing this child and how can I swiftly clear up this confusion so the child can move ahead independently, with clarity and confidence?

The teacher should avoid asking questions like:

- How can I drag this math problem out for the whole period so the slower students can catch up?
- How can I try to kill two birds with one stone and increase my students' writing skills by making them write their answers in full sentences?
- How can I follow the state or federal guidelines on how to present this topic even though I know this will confuse my particular students?
- How can I work in a lot of words that are not critical to the topic at hand in order to bolster the vocabularies of the third of my class who have recently arrived from other countries?
- How can I make this morning's math more culturally relevant by trying to entwine a lesson on racial prejudice with a lesson on linear equations?
- How can I get Tyrone and Stephen to get over the disagreement they had at recess by insisting they do this math problem together when they don't want to look at each other?
- How can I prepare my students for the real world by pairing up focused, hardworking scholarly students with hostile, disengaged drug-dealing students to solve quadratic equations?

~

Do not try to make math carry all these burdens. Allow math to stand on its own so children can appreciate its beauty and power and depth.

There is no shortage of complex and extremely challenging higher-level math. There is no need to take simple concepts that children can easily learn and turn them into exercises in bafflement and head-scratching. Let simple things be simple!

~

Here is an example of an awkward and confusing presentation of subtraction by a teacher and the effects of this later the same day:

Teacher: Okay class, today we are going to learn subtraction. [Writes 12 - 7 = __ on the board.] In order to subtract 7 from 12, we are going to break the bond of this 12 and turn it into 10 and 2. [Writes this below the 12.] Jarod, stop that! Now we are going to take the 7 from the 10 we got from the broken 12 and get 3 for an answer. Angel, look over here. We will take the 3 we just got and add it to the 2 we had left over from the broken bond of our original 12. Isabel and Rosie, stop talking! 3 plus 2 is five, so, as you can see, 12 take away 7 — which we can also call 12 minus 7 or 12 subtract 7 — is 5.

In this case, the teacher has been instructed by her school district to present subtraction in this way. This proposed method, however, demonstrates a glaring lack of understanding of how the minds of six and seven-year-olds work.

First of all, many children will wonder: why break the original 12 into 10 and 2 before trying to take something away?

Possible answers: "That's just how we do it."

Or: "Because our number system is base ten." … (Obvious next questions: "What's base ten? What's a number system?" While these are excellent topics, they should not be mixed in with presenting simple subtraction to first graders.)

Or: "Because 12 has a 10 and a 2 in it." (Possible next questions:

"But doesn't it also have a 5 and a 5 and a 2? And doesn't it have 11 and 1? In fact, doesn't it have lots of numbers in it?")

And then there's the matter of why subtract the 7 from the 10. A child might ask, "Why not take it away from the 2?"

Possible answers:

"No, no, we don't want to get into negative numbers right now ... we'll leave that for a few years."

Or: "Because we can." (A very weak answer.)

Next, children will wonder why we add the 3 we get from the 10 – 7 back onto the 2. Why not add it to the 12? Isn't that what we started with?

Possible answer:

"We did start with 12 but then we decided to break it into 10 and 2 for reasons we won't go into right now, so when we took our 7 from our 10 — and remember I said we'd leave the reason for that alone for now too — we want to add it to the 3 because that is the bit we didn't use."

This is a preposterously convoluted and confusing way of introducing subtraction. All attempts on behalf of the children to make sense of the method quickly generate ever-expanding areas of confusion.

~

Later that same day, in the home of one of the children, the aftereffects of this baffling presentation of subtraction play out:

Mother to 7-year-old daughter: Now Annie, don't you have some math homework?

Annie: No.

Mother: I see some here in your backpack.

Annie: I said *no*! No, I *don't*!

Mother: What's the matter, Sweetie? Let's take a look at it together.

Annie (sniffing): Okay.

Mother (relieved the assignment looks so easy): Okay, the first one is 15 − 8.

Annie looks warily at the worksheet and does not pick up her pencil.

Mother (encouragingly, trying to get Annie to put in the 7): Just write your answer here.

Annie: No! We can't just write the answer! This is math.

Mother: But you know 15 − 8. You learned your subtraction facts last year.

Annie: This isn't math facts. This is math *homework*.

Mother: Okay, you do it the way you are supposed to.

Annie: I can't remember how.

Mother (reaching for some nearby felt pens): Well, let's take 15 of these pens and take away …

Annie (getting agitated): It isn't about taking stuff away!

Mother: Well, it is a take away problem.

Annie: *No*, you have to break the bond of 15.

Mother (puzzled): Break the bond? What bond?

Annie: What *is* a bond?

Mother: A bond is when two things are stuck together.

Annie: Stop *confusing* me! Nothing is stuck together here!

Mother: Okay, let's look back at the question ....

Annie: You have to say 15 is something *else*.

Mother is silent, not wanting to make things worse.

Annie: You do it.

Mother: Something else like what?

Annie: I don't know! Like 13 and 2!

Mother: And then what?

Annie: Then you put those in boxes and take away 8. What is 2 take away 8? The teacher wouldn't say.

Mother: Well, it's down in the negatives. Negative six ... are you sure about this, Annie?

Annie: Not really. But maybe we can take the negative six you said and add it to 15. What's that?

Mother: 9.

Annie: Okay. That's the answer.

Mother: But you know it isn't. You know 15 – 8. Just last week you knew it.

Annie: It's 9. You said it yourself.

Mother: I did not. I only said -6 plus 15 was 9. Now let's go on to the next one … there are nineteen more of these!

Annie: I'm not doing anymore. I hate this. And it doesn't make sense. I hate math! Why was 15 – 8 equal to seven last week and now it's nine?

A far better way to teach children to present the problem 12 – 7 would be to provide every child with a laminated number line, taped to their desks. The teacher should then draw a similar number line on the board, and ask a sequence of questions along these lines:

Teacher: Who can read our problem? Billy?

Billy: 12 minus 7.

Teacher: Great. Now everyone, show me on your fingers what number this problem starts with.

The class shows 12 by flashing ten and then two on their fingers.

Teacher (moving her hand slowly along the number line): Show me a stop sign when I get to 12.

The class eagerly shoves their hands forward silently when the teacher gets to 12.

Teacher: Excellent. Now I am going to draw a big dot here on the 12. You do it too on your number lines.

The children pick up their erasable pens and mark 12 on their number lines.

Teacher: Show me on your fingers what number we are going to take away from 12. Yes! I see lots of 7's. To take away 7, we make 7 jumps. Do you think I will do the jumps this way [jumping from 12 to 13 to 14] or this way [moving hand from 12 to 11 to 10]?

Class (excitedly): That way!

Teacher: Going down?

Class: Yes!

Teacher: You're right. Taking away seven takes us down into the smaller numbers. Now I'm going to start taking jumps and you tell me when I've taken enough. One, two, three, four, five, six, seven…"

The class pushes forward their hands in stop signs when the teacher has done seven jumps.

Teacher: Perfect! You stopped me just in time. Where did we land? Show me on your fingers.

The class shows 5.

Teacher, smiling: Perfect. Now draw the seven jumps on *your* number lines.

The teacher circulates briskly and checks the children's work.

Teacher (back at the front): Let's do two more together.

The teacher leads the class in 15 – 9 = ___ and 11 – 8 = ___ at a slightly quicker pace, involving everyone.

Teacher: You're doing really well. Now I am going to give you a few to do on your own.

The teacher hands out a problem set with ten similar problems.

Sheila: I know the answers already! I don't need the number line.

Teacher: That's excellent. Only use the number line method if it helps you. If you can do it in your head, that's a very good way too. I'm putting extra math problems on this table for when you finish those.

~

Providing extra problems ensures that no child will be made to waste time or be "punished" with boredom for exhibiting competence. The extra problems should include questions like 16 - ___ = 7 and ___ - 5 = 8 so the children are drawn to think about subtraction more deeply. In addition, the children should be offered problems on a variety of topics, not just extra subtraction practice.

While the children are working, the teacher should move around the room checking how they are doing, offering encouragement and guidance as needed.

~

All that said, is there a place for "breaking up" numbers in first grade? Certainly, but this should be kept separate from learning a basic operation which every child needs to master and which should be kept as streamlined as possible. A failure to grasp subtraction will cause a child endless ongoing frustration in math, so the teacher's goal should be to make sure all the children understand it with no ambiguity. Simple subtraction is not the right sort of topic to choose for an open-ended discovery session.

The partitioning of numbers using a given number of summands (for example, how many ways can we get 6 by adding pairs of numbers?), on the other hand, is the perfect sort of topic for an open-ended exploration. It is a very enjoyable topic which children usually love, and it can stand on its own. If a child takes pleasure in the discussion yet does not grasp every nuance, this will not mathematically handicap her, as a failure to grasp subtraction would.

Here is an example of how to present partitioning to young children:

Teacher: Let's imagine that the only kind of numbers we know about are the numbers 0, 1, 2, 3, and so on. These numbers are called integers. [Writes *integer* on the board.] Who can give me another integer? Nathaniel?

Nathaniel: 100!

Teacher: Class, show me with your signals, do you think 100 is an integer?

The class shows agreement signals.

Teacher: Yes, it is. Everyone, show me another integer on your fingers. Good, I see Trel has a 7 and Juanita has a 10 and Annabel is flashing 30. Now, using only integers, let's find all the solutions we can for this equation: $\square + \Delta = 5$.

Children love this kind of problem and will eagerly generate solutions which the teacher can write on the board in the form of ordered pairs, near the equation.

Teacher: So, how many solutions did we find for $\square + \Delta = 5$?

Class holds up sixes.

Teacher: If we change our equation to $\square + \Delta = 7$, how many solutions do you think we can find? I want you to guess how many there will be before we try to find the solutions.

Children offer suggestions.

Teacher: Now let's find the solutions …

This is mathematical exploration for its own sake. The children's desire to figure it out will propel them forward. The teacher can ask deeper questions like:

- What if we were allowed to use other kinds of numbers for the solutions?
- What other kinds of numbers do you know about?
- What kinds of numbers might work?
- If we can use fractions, how many solutions could we find?
- Are there any other kinds of numbers we might use to solve this problem?

Children relish open-ended discovery and these kinds of discussions and explorations should be introduced very early on (kindergarten or first grade). The teacher should make a clear distinction in her own mind, though, between this kind of lesson and lessons with crisper edges. Children need to memorize math facts and master algorithms. These are two necessary components of their mathematical development.

Children should also be invited to delve into mathematical discovery in a playful yet artfully guided way. Exploring a topic like "How many solutions does this equation have if we only use numbers like zero, one, two, three?" and "Will the equation have more solutions if we allow ourselves to use different kinds of numbers?" will lead children to ponder the structure of math in a different way than if they are simply solving straightforward problems. This kind of exploration deepens their love of math and develops their thinking skills.

Children intuitively understand the difference between problems which can and should have a relatively simple solution (and a quick way to arrive at it) and questions which lend themselves to open-ended exploration. When they are given a problem like 750 divided by 15, they want to know how to get the answer efficiently. They know this is a completely different sort of question from one like, "Is there something bigger than infinity?" which they might eagerly discuss with mounting enthusiasm for half an hour or more, content to speculate and listen to others and debate, and not necessarily arrive at a solid conclusion.

19

THE LAYOUT AND AESTHETICS OF MATH PROBLEMS FOR CHILDREN

In Chapter 8, I touched on the challenge I was up against when I first realized that young children are capable of doing far more complex and interesting math than most people expect. If I presented the math at the board, all went well. I could make the concepts clear and inviting.

But when I wanted the children to work on their own so they could truly master the concepts by solving problems independently, I soon discovered that I could not find any math books that presented the kinds of problems I was teaching the children in a format that was accessible to children.

Most textbooks are written in a way that fails to take into account how children learn. However much we might wish that children would be perfectly willing to read wordy instructions, children are not. And however much we might like children to be enthusiastic about solving twenty-five problems, often using large and cumbersome numbers, on one topic before moving on to another topic, children usually won't be. Though we might like them to remember concepts they learned months or years ago and have not used since, they frequently won't. And while it might seem like a good use of a page to cram as much onto it as we possibly can, this will not work out well.

When it comes to children and math problems on a page, aesthetics is extremely important. The math problem, even if it is rich and complex, needs to look like a simple, clean, open door the child can step through. It should not look like a hoarder's paradise, with the front steps covered in broken clay pots of dead plants and hardened old shoes and the front porch all piled up with cracked leather basketballs and yellowed newspapers and outgrown rain boots and ruined umbrellas.

Textbook designers often think they will make math books more inviting if they add lots of photographs and illustrations and sidebars about "math in the real world". Unfortunately, this distracts children rather than drawing them in. The page sends their minds in too many directions, scattering their thinking.

I realised, as I began teaching my classes, that children are willing to do dramatically more work in an hour if the problems are uncluttered, inviting, have minimal instructions, and have plenty of white space around them. All the things that might cause the child to look away from the math, or get into a conversation, or daydream or snap a pencil in half or write on the desk, need to be cleared away so that all that is left on the page is something the child will want to dive into right away.

I began formatting the problems in a new way. I would take a blank 8.5 x 11-inch piece of paper and fold it into quarters to create both a horizontal and vertical line through the middle of the page. In each quarter, I wrote either a problem or a small set of similar problems.

~

Wording

I kept my instructions to a bare minimum, knowing that some children are very good at math but have reading challenges. The words were intended to spring everyone into the problem, not form a wall to keep part of the class away from the problem. Every time I wrote an instruction, I imagined myself as a child trying to make sense of it.

Even children who can read very well generally do not like reading wordy instructions and will often ignore them. They like to plunge in.

With this in mind, I always used the bare minimum of words that would clearly convey what needed to be done. All math problems should be phrased in a way that maximizes the amount of time the child spends actually *doing* math. If a phrase can be condensed down to one word, it should be. If a single word of instruction will suffice, then nothing should be added to this. If whole sentences are used, they should be precise and grammatically correct, with no ambivalence whatsoever as to their meaning. It should be immediately obvious what one is intended to do. Sometimes it works best to simply giving one boxed example showing how to solve a problem, instead of instructions, followed by a few similar problems for the child to solve.

~

Variety

On each quarter of the page, I would put a different category of math. The top left-hand quarter was often devoted to a set of ten equations. Another quarter might be a geometry problem, another a small matrix logic problem, and the fourth a number theory problem.

There are three main reasons to offer children different types of math during a class period.

The first is that children greatly prefer this. They like variety. A group of children will be far happier solving twenty equations, two number theory questions, a few geometry problems, a topology problem, and two logic problems in an hour than they would be doing exclusively sums, or one-variable equations. Children will concentrate for longer and accomplish more if they are given the opportunity to work on a variety of types of math during a class period.

The second reason is that this practice of offering children a variety of types of math each day keeps every kind of math alive for them. When children spend a year on algebra and then don't do any algebra the following year, they tend to forget a lot of what they have learned.

The third reason is that working on a variety of types of math makes children's minds more nimble and forces them to practice, over and over during a class period, figuring out what category of math each problem or small problem set falls into and what kind of techniques would be best suited to this kind of problem. Determining what kind of problem one is up against is a different level of skill from following an instruction from a teacher like, "Here's how you find the area of a triangle. Find the area of these 30 triangles and then put your math books away."

Shifting back and forth between the different kinds of thought processes required to solve a wide variety of algebra and geometry and logic and computation problems helps children develop into more flexible and adept problem solvers. More pathways, and stronger pathways, get formed in their brains.

~

Introducing new math vocabulary

I deliberately introduced new math vocabulary in a way that required the children to work actively with the new word rather than simply telling them, "These are parallel lines," and pointing to a pair on the board. Most children will quickly forget a new term if they do not use it immediately.

For example, I might give a problem which shows a box , filled with a variety of pairs of parallel lines and labelled "These are parallel," followed by a collection of non-parallel lines labeled, "These are NOT parallel." Below this, there would be a mixture of parallel and non-parallel lines and the direction, "Circle the ones that are parallel." At the bottom of this little problem set, I might add, "Does the word parallel contain anything that is parallel? If so, circle that part of the word." (This will help children remember how to spell the word.) A problem of this type forces the child to begin working with the concept of parallel rather than passively observing the teacher showing a knowledge of the term at the board.

Other terms like isosceles triangle can be treated in a similar way. When children are required to understand a new word in order to solve a problem, they are far more likely to remember the word.

In future classes, I would keep the new word fresh in their minds with problems where I would show a collection of different shapes with the instructions:

- Shade the isosceles triangles.
- Put stripes in the equilateral triangles.
- Put dots in the trapezoids.

In order to commit concepts or terms to long-term memory, most children need to use them over and over.

The primary goal of a math problem

Math problems should be phrased in such a way that the child is most likely to reason soundly and arrive at the right answer. Problems should never contain awkward phrasings, unclear terms, or unnecessary information (unless this is intentional) because this creates a numbing effect on the child.

Remember: when a child repeatedly succeeds with something independently, she gets better and better at it. We *want* children to succeed over and over, not get constantly bogged down and confused.

Writing math problems for children takes considerable skill and practice. Many math tests and math books appear to have been written by people who have no idea how children's minds work.

Having a degree or two or even three in math education may seem to qualify a person to write a math curriculum — but what is most critical is having direct experience watching and helping children from a wide variety of backgrounds solve problems and seeing, with one's own eyes, what works and what doesn't.

Some math books might work very well if every child in the room was at the same grade level, spoke English fluently, could read well, and worked at an average pace. However, in all my years of teaching, I have never worked in a classroom where all those conditions were met. I have taught in twenty public schools in Berkeley, Oakland, and Richmond, and I have taught in a residential psychiatric center for young children in San Francisco. I have taught on a First Nations Reservation in Canada, and I've taught children at UC Berkeley. In every one of those classrooms, there was tremendous variety. Ideally, a person writing math problems should see how a wide range of children respond to the problems and make adjustments based on direct feedback. A very important part of this is seeing not just which problems are clear and manageable to children, but which ones inspire joy and delight, and making certain to include a generous supply of the latter.

~

Learning to deal with badly worded questions

There is some value in teaching children to recognize when there is unnecessary information in a problem or to recognize that a critical piece of information is missing. Children enjoy this — but in the right context. If it is a fun challenge, they will be up for it — but children do not like to be ambushed by this sort of thing. They do not like to encounter confusingly-worded problems when grappling with a new concept, or in the middle of trying to complete their homework, or while taking an exam.

To help children hone the skill of not being distracted by unnecessary information or of not working away for ages on a problem that lacks some critical piece of information, the teacher can teach this explicitly. For example:

Teacher: I'm going to read you a problem and I want you to listen carefully and then raise your hands and tell me what information is unnecessary for solving the problem … Here's the problem: "Jenny and Isabella went into a small store with a dirty front door. In the store, they saw three friends — Isaiah, Rufus, and Leasha. Jenny spent four dollars and fifty cents and Isabella spent five dollars and fifty cents. The store had chocolate bars on sale for seventy-five cents. How much money did the two girls spend all together?" Okay, now remember, I don't want an answer to the problem yet. I just want to know what information was unnecessary.
There will be an eager waving of hands at this point.
Teacher: Amar?
Amar: We don't need to know how much the chocolate bars cost! We don't even know if they wanted chocolate bars.
Teacher: Very good … what else? Taiye?"
Taiye, laughing: Why would we need to know if the door was dirty!
Teacher: Would that help us at all, class?
Class: No!!
Teacher: Was there any other unnecessary information? Charles?
Charles: We didn't need to know that they met three friends in the store because the problem never asks us anything about the friends. And we don't need to know the friends' names.

This type of discussion helps children to read more critically and cut to the heart of a problem.

20

TEACHING A NEW SKILL: ISOLATE, THEN EMBED

Whenever I teach a new concept, I try to isolate it— conceptually, visually, and linguistically — from anything that could possibly make it harder than it needs to be for a child.

For example, if I want to teach a child how exponents work, I start with the simplest possible numbers which can convey the concept. I never stir in a real-life situation which might distract the child from the pure math. I don't use big numbers which require elaborate computation skills or a calculator, and I never use fractions or decimals.

I want the concept to stand out starkly so I avoid entangling it with anything that might trip up the child or divert their attention away from the concept. I particularly want to avoid any words or instructions which might push the child away from the essence of the concept.

Exponents, in an ordinary textbook, might be introduced on a crowded page which could contain two thousand symbols (letters, numbers, punctuation) as well as sidebars, and maybe a photograph. A page or two later, before a child has completely mastered how a simple exponent works, he may be asked to square 3/4, or find .73 cubed.

What happens to the child who is overwhelmed by too much information on the page? To the child who does not know how to multiply fractions? To the child who does not know how to multiply decimals? He fails to learn exponents and adds one more experience of frustration and failure into his bank of math miseries. This is completely unnecessary. A child with very minimal computation skills is fully capable of understanding the concept of exponents and there is no need to exclude the child from grasping the concept by unnecessarily mixing in fractions or decimals right at the start.

After the children have mastered the basic concept, I then embed the concept in a variety of problems — still using relatively small numbers — so they get lots of practice using it. Only after the child fully grasps the concept (and has shown mastery of decimals and fractions) would I ask the child to square a decimal or find the cube root of a fraction. By using this method, I frequently had children in my classes who by the age of nine could take the cube root of 8/27 or raise 1/2 to the fifth power in their heads as quickly and easily as they could add small numbers.

21

STUDENTS WORKING TOGETHER: THE DISASTERS

It is important to separate absurdities from practicalities with regard to students working together. There are ways to set up a classroom so students can genuinely help each other and both the helpers and the helped will benefit greatly. There are ways to harness the energy and enthusiasm of the entire class to deepen understanding and develop other skills at the same time.

Unfortunately, the most common ways that students are required to work together in math class do not have any of these benefits.

Having students work together on math problems in small groups or pairs sounds lovely in theory. Different students will contribute different ideas which together will enable them to come up with a solution they might not have been able to arrive at individually, more advanced students will deepen their understanding by explaining concepts and ideas to struggling students, and struggling students will receive more help than they would get if everyone worked alone on the same problems and the teacher tried to race around the room helping everyone who was confused.

That's the idea teachers get sold on and which parents are told about. This might work if the groups were discussing a topic like, "If your group was going to be left on a desert island for a year and you could only take ten items with you, what would they be?" The group could start debating this and try to arrive, by consensus, at a list of ten things. Everyone would be on equal footing. Not only that, if a group of six children arrived at a list like "Game console, generator, computer games, fresh water, ..." and left off an item that another group might have thought vitally important such as matches, no harm would come of this. There is no right answer to the question and the whole point of the exercise is to get children debating and explaining and persuading and listening. As long as it does not devolve into a physical fight or harsh insults, nothing can go too wrong because nothing is at stake.

But let's look carefully at what actually happens when a group of children with widely varying math skills attempts to work together to solve a single problem or get the day's math assignment done.

First of all, something *is* at stake here: the children's math education. If this group work were to take place only once or twice a year, it wouldn't matter very much if it did not work out well. But there are schools where all math work is group work, year after year.

~

Example 1: a small group in a seventh grade classroom

Consider a group consisting of five seventh-grade students: twelve-year-old Jason whose math skills are at about fifth-grade level, eleven year old Natalie whose math skills are ninth- grade level, thirteen year old Hunter whose math skills are at third-grade level, twelve year old Isabella whose math level is fourth-grade on some topics and fifth and sixth-grade on others, and twelve year old Simon whose math level is seventh-grade. Hunter has been diagnosed with ADHD and Simon with a high-functioning Autism Spectrum Disorder.

This group of five children has been asked to solve a set of ten problems. The first problem states:

> *The reading on a pressure valve decreases from 36 psi to 30 psi. What is the percent decrease in pressure? (Round your answer to the nearest tenth of a percent.) Explain your answer.*

"What does psi mean?" asks Simon.

No one in the group knows though Natalie understands from context that it is a unit of measure.

"It's how much pressure there is," she tells Simon.

"But what does it mean?" Simon repeats. "All words mean something."

"She just told you!" says Hunter. "Don't start that everything-means-something shit."

One feature of Simon's Autism Spectrum Disorder involves his wanting to know the precise definitions of all new words he hears. He gets extremely agitated if this is thwarted and Hunter, who has agitation problems of his own, knows this and likes to wind up Simon.

"Shit is feces," says Simon. "I am not starting anything to do with feces."

"I said *not* to start that everything-means-something shit!" says Hunter more loudly.

The teacher hears the word shit and rushes over to tell Hunter to watch his language.

"He won't shut up about that weird word thing he has," Hunter complains.

"Remember we talked about tolerating differences," the teacher says. "Now get to work on the problem."

"What's a pressure valve?" asks Jason.

"Like that black thing on a bike tire," says Natalie who has already solved the first three problems while the other children were talking.

"So how do we do this?" asks Isabella.

"Six percent is the answer," says Jason. "It went from 36 to 30. Six. Let's do the next one."

"That's not percent," points out Isabella.

Natalie, who knows from months of experience that trying to explain percents to her team never accomplishes anything because most of them don't understand fractions, is now on problem 7.

"I'm putting 16.7," says Hunter who is sitting right next to Natalie. "That's what Natalie put so it must be right."

Just then the teacher, Mr. Evian, appears beside the group. "I told you not to rush on ahead of your group," he says sternly to Natalie. "Erase your answers and this time stick together with your group. And you didn't write how you arrived at your answers."

Extremely annoyed but not showing it, Natalie erases all her answers, returns to the first problem, and says to the group, "You put the change in pressure on the top of the fraction and the original pressure on the bottom …"

Hunter is bored by this and says to Simon, "Psi, psi, psi," pronouncing psi as "piss".

"What? What?" says Simon. "Why are you saying that to me? First you said shit and now you are saying piss! Those aren't classroom words!"

Hunter smirks and says, "Psi in the classroom."

"Shut up! Shut up! Shut up!" says Simon shrilly.

"You shut up. I'm trying to listen to Natalie," says Hunter.

"You put the change in pressure on top," Natalie repeats.

"But why put the first pressure on the bottom?" asks Isabella.

"We're supposed to be finding the percentage change," says Natalie."So you have to use the pressure you started with."

"Huh?" says Jason. "What's that got to do with percent?"

"You make that fraction equal to x over a hundred to find the percent," says Natalie.

"What does percent mean again?" asks Jason.

"Parts per hundred," says Simon, relaxing slightly. He does not know how to solve the problem but he does know the definition of percent.

"This problem has nothing to do with a hundred," says Jason.

"That's what we're trying to do!" says Natalie, starting to lose patience.

"If Natalie wrote 16.7 in the first place then that's what it is. Who cares about percents!" says Hunter.

"That *is* the percent," says Natalie.

"What do we put for "explain your work"?" asks Isabella, writing 16.7.

"Put Natalie said so," laughs Jason.

"No, really," says Isabella.

Natalie writes on her paper: I set up equivalent fractions and cross-multiplied and then divided to get the percentage change. Isabella writes this too and so does Simon.

The teacher circles back and says, "Good work, group! That's excellent the way you are working together now."

The group "work" goes on like this until the bell rings for lunch.

What went wrong?

For one thing, no one in the group learned anything at all. Natalie, who already knew exactly how to solve the problems swiftly, learned nothing new and did not derive any satisfaction from teaching others because the levels and challenges of her group were too varied and complex for her to be able to provide any meaningful help. Had she been allowed to do some more advanced problems on her own and devote a few minutes to explaining to Isabella how to solve the percent problems, this would have worked fine. Isabella had the necessary skills to begin to understand the problems but the other members of the group needed to learn how to work with fractions. They would likely need months of learning concepts from earlier grades before the percent problems would have any real meaning to them.

The combination of Hunter's ADHD and Simon's Autism Spectrum Disorder resulted in Hunter easing his own discomfort over being unable to solve the problems by provoking Simon. Hunter needed direct instruction at his level (third grade), without the distraction of conversing with several confused children. Simon needed direct instruction at his grade level (seventh) from someone who understood how to keep him focused, or from a computer.

At the end of the lesson, all the students had written down the correct answers, worked out by Natalie, and most of the children had also written down Natalie's explanations for how she had arrived at the answers, but because the other children did not understand the meaning of terms like "cross multiply and then divide", they were no further ahead. Three of the group members did not know how to perform a basic division problem, let alone a division problem in which they had to figure out what numbers needed to be divided. All the students in the group were given back their papers the next day with an A on the top corner — yet four of the five children would not have been able to solve a single one of the problems independently.

~

Example 2: a pair working together in a tenth grade classroom

Let's consider a second example of students working together. In this case, it is a tenth-grade class and all the students are required to work in pairs. Sixteen-year-old Justin has been paired for the last week with fifteen-year-old Sarah. The class has just started a section on hyperbolas.

Today's assignment starts with the question:

> *Find the center, vertices, foci, eccentricity, and asymptotes of the hyperbola with the given equation, and sketch* $y^2/25 - x^2/144 = 1$.

"How are we supposed to do this?" Justin asks. There are numerous skills needed to solve the problem and Justin has not yet learned most of them.

Sarah wishes she could help Justin, but all attempts to do so over the last five math lessons have failed. She is also expected to complete the assignment herself and is very much hoping to get an A in the class so she can get into Honors Precalculus next year. She lacks the tools and the time to get to the bottom of Justin's confusion.

Instead, she leans over and says, "You start by looking at this first denominator. Notice that it is 25 so *a* must equal 5 ..."

"Huh?" says Justin. "I don't see an *a*."

"The *a* is in the standard form of the equation for a hyperbola ... the a^2 goes under the y^2."

"What's a hyperbola?"

"It's one of the conic sections."

"Comic whats?"

Sarah, in being asked to sit beside Justin and being told to work together, is being asked to do what the school itself and the teacher of the class have failed to do: figure out what is preventing Justin from understanding high school level math and provide him with the remediation he needs. If the high school, with its power to test and offer resources to Justin over a period of years, and the teacher, who has a degree in math and a degree in education and has been teaching for seventeen years, are unable to meet the challenge, how is a fifteen-year-old with no training expected to help Justin in a meaningful way?

As Sarah tries to help, she realizes that everything she says to Justin only raises a fresh area of confusion.

"Imma pop a xan," interrupts Justin as Sarah is trying to explain squaring. "This shit hard."

Justin lives in the Berkeley Hills with his mother who is an English professor and his father who is an environmental engineer. Though Justin spoke in a style very much like his parents until age fourteen when he started at Berkeley High School, he has adopted and perfected a new speech pattern over the last eighteen months. He takes a small ball of foil from an already eaten chocolate out of his pocket and picks at it to expose a Xanax which he swallows with an exaggerated gulp.

Sarah's job soon becomes even harder. She shifts her focus back to her own work but before long the teacher, Mr. Weissler, passes by her desk and Justin's and notices she is on the tenth problem and Justin is still on the first.

"Sarah, you're supposed to be working together," chastises Mr. Weissler. "Justin, if you're stuck, ask your partner for help," he adds.

A few desks away, Jameesha is waving her hand for help and Mr. Weissler walks away toward her.

About fifteen minutes have passed now since Justin took the Xanax. He looks sleepy and relaxed. Trying to oblige the teacher, who allots 20% of the course grade to classroom participation which means Sarah's grade will come down from an A to a B if she does not adequately help Justin each day, Sarah turns to Justin and says, "Do you want me to help you some more with the first one?"

"Iss good," says Justin, smiling, his pupils widely dilated and his pencil on the floor.

We can't hand over to children the difficult task of educating other children whom we ourselves have failed to reach, giving the helper-children no more tools to get the job done than we have allowed ourselves. It doesn't work.

Yet within a classroom, we have an undeniable and vast resource: the potential for children to inspire and help each other. They are indeed capable of this, but we need to set up the classroom in such a way that they will succeed when they work together. As we saw above, asking Natalie to bring along a group of children whom the school failed to keep at grade level by sitting a few of these children with her and telling her to get on with it serves no useful purpose and wastes a great deal of everyone's time.

Likewise, telling Justin, who is six years behind Sarah in math, to "work together" with her on a problem far beyond his level is too vague an instruction and one he cannot comply with. Is he supposed to be aware of all the skills he is lacking and ask Sarah to teach him those instead of attempting the day's assignment? Most teachers don't have a clear sense of the skills each child in the room is lacking, so requiring this level of self-awareness of a failing child who is many years below grade level is unrealistic.

Sarah's task is just as impossible as Justin's. It would take years to teach Justin the skills he has failed to master. He did well in math when his family lived in Massachusetts, but when he was in fourth grade his family moved to Berkeley and math suddenly became confusing for Justin. He was no longer taught clear ways to do things like multiply or divide. Some of these things he'd thought he had understood, but his new teacher told him not to do them that way anymore.

He could vaguely remember now that he once knew how to multiply and divide, but in his Berkeley classroom he was told to use something called lattice multiplication which never made any sense to him. When his mother went and spoke with the teacher, the teacher explained to her that the class was emphasizing deep conceptual understanding and that the point was not to learn how to multiply and divide using standard algorithms but rather to explore a variety of ways to perform these operations. Division was taught in a long and complicated way that involved guessing, over and over, how many of something might go into something else and subtracting the guess from some other number as well as keeping a tally of the guesses. This long roundabout method never clicked for Justin. Almost overnight he went from being a good math student to being a very poor one. In fifth grade, things got even worse.

Middle School was better, from Justin's point of view, because he discovered that he could smoke marijuana behind the kitchen portable just before math class. Magically, his embarrassment over not being able to keep up in class vanished. His grades dropped from C's to D's but the same amazing anesthetic blocked out the discomfort of that as well. When his parents fretted and questioned him and offered a tutor, and when his dad tried to help him, and when he was called into his math classroom after school to meet with his parents and the teacher, he kept himself detached from the discomfort of this scrutiny and attention by smoking more often. Then, at the beginning of tenth grade, a friend gave him a Xanax. When he took it just after lunch, already high on weed, he could hardly believe how little he cared about math. He was no more bothered by not knowing what an extraneous solution was than he was by some shopping carts under the freeway overpass near Costco.

Was Sarah really expected to unravel all these problems that plagued poor Justin? And was it fair and reasonable to lower Sarah's math grade to a B if she failed to help him, thus preventing her from taking Honors Pre-calculus the following year?

22

STUDENTS WORKING TOGETHER: THE TRIUMPHS

How can a teacher set up her classroom so students genuinely *can* work together productively?

The most effective way to do this is to create a non-competitive atmosphere in which every child is expected to do her best at her own level, and helping others is encouraged. In this kind of a classroom, children will naturally help each other. Most of this helping and asking for help will simply unfold on its own but the teacher can help facilitate it by having a whiteboard devoted to students writing their names and listing topics they have mastered which they would like to teach to others. A student wanting help with multiplying fractions or finding the volume of cylinders and cones could scan this list for someone who is eager to explain these things.

~

Here is an example of how this would work:

In Ms. Channing's fifth grade class, everyone works on Khan Academy during math period. Isabella started the year well below grade level in math. Her family has moved five times since she was born. She missed quite a bit of school in third grade when she had a series of ear infections, and went to a school for fourth grade which emphasized art and minimized math. Her initial assessment on Khan Academy revealed a number of gaps. Charisse, who sits two seats over from Isabella, has always been strong in math. She has mastered most of seventh-grade math and is just finishing up five remaining topics. Charisse loves explaining math to other children.

On this particular morning, Charisse has just mastered finding the volume of triangular prisms. Nearby, Isabella is confused by an exercise which involves determining if numbers are prime or composite or neither. She thought she'd understood this topic and thought 1 was a prime but when she puts in this answer she finds she is wrong. She knows she could watch the Khan video on this topic but she is aware that she learns most easily when the teacher or a classmate explain something to her. Isabella has noticed that Charisse has put her name on the list saying she can explain any topics up through sixth grade so she walks over to Charisse's desk and asks if she will explain why one is neither a prime nor a composite number.

Charisse remembers being puzzled about this herself and is happy to explain it to Isabella. Isabella brings over her chair and Charisse, who has been trained by the classroom teacher to ask questions when trying to explain a concept, asks Isabella for two examples of primes and two examples of composites. Isabella is able to answer these questions easily, which helps Charisse understand better what is confusing Isabella.

After clearing up the matter of 1, Charisse, a natural teacher, poses the question, "What about zero? Do you think it is prime, composite, or neither?" The two girls work together for a few minutes and then Isabella thanks Charisse for the help. Charisse, feeling pleased that her helping of Isabella went so well, tells Isabella she can come over and ask for help whenever she needs it. Isabella heads back to her desk, puts in that 1 is neither prime nor composite and understands why, finishes that section after several more questions, and moves on to a new topic. Charisse returns to her own work.

~

Why did this pair work together so much more effectively than the Justin/Sarah pair described in the last chapter?

Isabella was working at her real level, not several grades above it. Charisse was also allowed to work at her real level, not two years below it. Isabella knew exactly what she needed help with; because she was working on Khan Academy, she received immediate feedback on whether she was getting the right answers rather than finishing a worksheet incorrectly, handing it in at the end of the class (or not at all) and possibly getting it back a few days later showing she had made a few mistakes.

Isabella wanted to understand how to get the right answer, not just copy someone else's work or brush the matter aside. She turned to a classmate who was both able and willing to help with that particular topic.

Isabella's request of Charisse was specific ("Can you help me understand why 1 is neither a prime nor a composite?") Because the ongoing feedback on Khan Academy had told her she understood how to classify numbers other than 1 such as 5 and 18 and 40 in this regard, she was not posing a vague question like, "I just don't get this prime stuff! Can you help?"

Charisse was free to say, "Yes, I can help you" or, "I just need to finish these three problems and then I will come over to your desk and help you," or even, "I can help you tomorrow but today I just want to work on my own math." Helping another person was a choice, not an obligation.

Charisse, along with the rest of her class, had received training from the classroom teacher in how to help others with math (ask questions, identify as best you can what is confusing the person, ask further questions to make sure the person really understands, don't go too fast, use pencil and paper not just words so the explanation is visual as well as verbal).

The classroom was set up by the teacher to encourage this kind of seeking of help and offering of help. Students were allowed to talk quietly about math. They were allowed to get out of their seats to get help or offer help but not to distract anyone else or waste time.

Isabella was successfully helped by Charisse which reinforced her sense that asking for specific help from the right person is very useful. Her understanding of the math topic was deepened. She was able to move ahead rather than stay stuck. Feeling confident that she could move through confusion, she returned to her desk and solved forty-five more problems before the end of the class period.

Charisse felt useful. She enjoyed helping Isabella and was glad that she had worked hard on her math to the point that she could be of service to other kids. In explaining the topic to Isabella, she reviewed it for herself and was more likely to retain it over the long run. She was developing a valuable communication skill — helping a peer without talking down to the person or making her feel embarrassed or inadequate.

The Justin/Sarah situation failed to work because Justin was so far out of his depth that he knew his only hope was to copy Sarah's answers. His requests for help were half-hearted at best. He knew he was supposed to ask how to do the problems rather than bluntly saying, "Let me write down your answers" but he also knew he was not going to understand whatever explanation Sarah might offer. Justin's requests were vague: "How do you do this?" and "Huh?"

Though Sarah wanted to be of help Justin, she was in no position to do so. She did not know what skills he was missing or have time to figure this out.

Justin's use of a benzodiazepine during class further complicated the situation. He needed help for substance abuse but Sarah, not the teacher, was aware that he was high in class and would not have been able to take in any concepts even if she had been able to get to the bottom of his mathematical confusion. Not only was she expected to set aside her own work to try to help Justin when he had just put himself outside the range of being able to do any math that period, she had the added burden of knowing he was using a drug that could have killed him if it had been a home-pressed Xanax laced with Fentanyl, and not knowing whether she should tell someone.

~

Small group work

Getting students to work in small groups is even more challenging than having them work in pairs because it is much easier for this to lead to enormous amounts of time being wasted. Children who are intently focused on solving math problems are not generally drawn to working simultaneously with a number of other students. Children like to learn by doing, and when five or six children push their desks together to do the same problem or set of problems, a good portion of the time for any given student in the group is spent passively. In order for small group work to be genuinely useful, the students in the group would need to all be at close to the same level and all able to focus without distracting each other. These two conditions are rarely met in small group work situations.

In general, math problem-solving time is best spent working independently and seeking help whenever the need arises and offering help whenever a child wishes to offer it. Even if students are focused primarily on working independently, there will still be plenty of opportunities to have enjoyable and productive exchanges with classmates, in the form of asking for and offering help, comparing solutions, or sharing an interesting discovery.

23

GROUP WORK GUIDED BY THE TEACHER

There is great value in regularly having the entire class focus on one math topic or problem. It is unifying, energizing, and peaceful to have everyone directing their attention to the same problem. It brings together a busy group of children who have been working at their own levels.

The purpose of group work is to enjoy the company of others, learn how to exchange ideas in a respectful way, pool ideas and insights, and take joy in interesting conversation. This kind of collaboration can stimulate children to see things in new ways, explore, debate, and experiment.

In order for group work (in this case meaning the whole class working together on the same problem) to be a productive use of everyone's time, the lesson needs to be skillfully guided by the teacher who must present the topic at the board and involve every member of the class. If children are told to work on math in groups and then left to get on with it without direct guidance, most students will learn very little. Similarly, if the teacher presents the topic at the board and only calls on a few students, most of the class will learn next to nothing.

How can the teacher guide the entire class on a problem,

though, in a way that does not bore and waste the time of a third of the class and baffle and confuse another third, if the students in the class are at a variety of different levels?

Choosing topics for a discovery-style presentation to the whole class

The key is to choose a topic or problem which is new to everyone and accessible to all. An area I often chose for this at the start of class was logic. I would compose a complicated logic problem (often in the form of a mystery) before each class and, standing at the board, lead the whole class in solving it.

This gave a sense of focus and unity to the group. It enabled everyone in the class to participate. I embedded math within the logic problem — but not math which required years of skills some of the children lacked.

For example, a clue in the logic puzzle might be: "All the suspects' ages were in the Fibonacci Sequence." In a class which had not worked with the Fibonacci Sequence before, I would write the first five or six terms on the board and then have the children figure out how each term was generated and ask them to show on their fingers the next few terms until we had the sequence up on the board as high as was reasonable for human ages. If any children in the class were unsure how the sequence worked, I would call on a child to explain how the terms were generated to be sure everyone understood.

Another clue in the logic problem might be, "The thief's age was a perfect number," or, "The age difference between Sam and his sister was an even prime." Each of these sorts of clues would involve brief discussions or clarifications about what a perfect number was, or how many even primes there were.

The type of clue I would not give would be one such as, "The thief's age was a root of the quadratic $x^2 + 24x - 52 = 0$" if the class was, for example, fifth grade. While one or two students in the class might have been able to figure this out, the math involved would be inaccessible to many of the children.

As we were working together to solve the logic problem, I would praise students for their explanations, draw things on the board to make parts of the problem clearer, and model this technique for the class. If clue 5 told us that Brendan was older than Tara and clue 11 told us that Tara was older than Bryce, and clue 13 told us the thief was younger than Bryce, I would order these names on the board in a vertical column to make it clear whom we could eliminate as suspects.

Rather than lecturing, I would model for the students how to break down multi-part problems, whether they were logic problems with many clues or algebra problems with many steps, into small manageable chunks.

With a series of carefully chosen questions, I led the students to think in mathematically efficient ways. Even if I were explicitly showing them a useful technique, I would fill the demonstration with questions so they would feel they were discovering the technique and using it. Though I was actually carefully guiding all of them rather than having some of the children stumble on a way of solving the problem, my questions took them out of the passive role and led them to generate by the means of solving the problem and the solution. This results in a deeper level of understanding and confidence which makes children more likely to be able to arrive at solutions on their own when given problems to solve independently.

How does one do all this without having a handful of students dominate the discussion and most of the children sink into silence? By asking dozens and dozens of questions of varying levels of difficulty and requiring ongoing feedback from the class in response to these questions. "Show me on your fingers how many years older Sam is than Brendan." "Show me with your arm signals, could Elisa's twin be twelve?' "How many faces does a cube have? Show me on your fingers. And what about a hexagonal pyramid?"

Spending time at the board presenting how to add fractions to a fifth-grade class in which half the class already knows how to do this

would not meet the criteria of choosing a topic that would be of value to everyone, though if the class needed to add two fractions to make use of a clue in a logic problem and this was gone over briefly, it would be fine.

Another kind of math problem, besides logic, which could be taught to the whole class is the kind which can be solved both visually and algebraically. An example of this would be: "Brenda has 10 animals. Some are chickens and some are horses. Altogether her animals have 32 legs. How many are chickens and how many are horses?"

Depending on the range of levels in the class, the teacher could present just the visual method to the class, or both methods.

24

KEEPING THE CLASS FOCUSED WHILE LEADING A GROUP DISCOVERY TOPIC

Some aspects of a math class should be flexible and spontaneous. No child should be rushed or slowed down while learning. If a child develops a faster or more intuitive way of solving a problem, this should be encouraged. If a child asks a question which opens up a new area of enquiry during a class discussion, the teacher should allow the discussion to move there is she judges it useful.

There is one aspect of teaching, though, where I allow no flexibility whatsoever. When I am leading a class in the discovery of a concept or the solution of a problem at the board, I do not allow any talking by anyone other than the one person who is supposed to be talking (unless I have asked for the entire class to respond in unison). I do not allow any side conversations or whispering exchanges, whether they are about math or not, and I do not allow any distracting activities to go on at the same time as the explanation or discussion, including by adults who might be observing the class or assisting with the class in some way.

The reason for this is that even seemingly minor distractions fragment the focus. A vitally important quality which excellent math students possess is the capacity to focus intensely. The brain can learn this through practice, and an excellent opportunity to practice this is during teacher-led group learning time.

Every time I meet with a new class of children, I make every child in the room a name tag out of a folded large index card on which I write their name in large capitals with a thick black permanent marker and require everyone to have their name tag facing me on their desk. This enables me to address everyone by name, even on the first day of class, and also helps me learn their names more quickly.

The instant I notice that a child is talking at the same time as I am explaining something, or at the same time as the child I have just called on, I stop the class and calmly but firmly (never raising my voice and never expressing annoyance) address by name the child who is not supposed to be talking: "Ella, please stop talking." I never persist with my math explanation, talking over the distraction and hoping it will end soon. If a child is answering my question and another child gets into a side conversation, I first politely ask the child I called on to pause and then I address the talker in a matter of fact way. "Stephen, please stop talking. I have called on Micah."

This rule, of only one person talking at a time during group discovery math time, is made crystal clear on the first day of class and is held to with no exceptions. If someone is rhythmically kicking a desk leg, or thwacking a ruler, or making any other kind of distracting sound, I use the same method of pausing the lesson, addressing the noise and making sure it stops, and then immediately picking up right where we left off.

I do not lecture or explain or attempt to justify in any way why I want the room focused. The importance of a well-focused classroom is self-evident and any debate about the need for focus is itself a distraction. With a bare minimum of words and emotion, I swiftly restore order.

This might seem like making a big deal about something very trivial. Why stop the flow of the lesson for twenty-eight people in order to address the whispering of two children? Isn't calling attention to the whispering and pausing the lesson more distracting?

In the moment, yes. But if two children in a classroom are

allowed to whisper, it won't be long at all before it is four people whispering and then ten people talking. If a classroom teaching assistant opens a stack of mail, slicing open each envelope with a letter-opener while the teacher is showing the class how to find the sum of the first one hundred integers, soon a child in the room will be snapping open his binder rings to rearrange his notes and someone else will start tapping a pencil against a desk leg, and then two children will be talking, and someone will start watching a fly trapped inside the window instead of looking at the board.

Distracting noises in a classroom are like clutter magnets in a house. If a stairway landing has nothing on it, it will generally stay this way. But if a small table is placed there, there will soon be a backpack on it. Then it will be the backpack and a tea mug with an inch of milky tea in the bottom, and then those items pushed to the back and a stack of clean laundry wedged at the front, and then someone's hoodie draped over the top of the clean laundry. This growing pile of random items may not bother anyone or come with any cost — but distractions spreading across a math class do come with a cost. Before long, quite a few of the children will no longer be paying any attention to the lesson, and the teacher will have her attention divided and won't be teaching in peak form to those children who are still trying to learn. If the situation reaches the level where multiple distractions have broken out, each distraction can carry on under the cover of the rest. If the teacher addresses one commotion, because there are already five others and the room is starting to seem chaotic, several more can spring up while she is trying to get that one under control.

The solution to this is to address the very first moment of the first distraction and nip it in the bud, even if it seems like too small a matter to bother with.

This photo shows a child who is both intently focused and completely at ease as she listens to an algebra question. Though there are thirty ten-year-olds in the class, there are no distracting sounds or activities and she can hear without having to strain or filter out noise and bustle. All her energy can go into learning.

An added benefit of maintaining this level of order is that it is much easier to elicit feedback from the entire class — a process which is crucial to the success of any presentation at the board — when every child has their eyes and attention on the teacher and the math. When the teacher asks the whole class to show the cube root of negative eight on their fingers, the only way she will know who is understanding and who isn't is to get a response from every single student in the room, whether that response is the correct answer, a wrong answer, or the "I'm not sure" signal.

When students are solving problems at their desks, I allow them to talk quietly among themselves so they can help each other, but as

I move around the room checking on progress and offering help, I redirect back to the math every activity that is not problem-solving and every conversation that is not mathematical.

25

TEACHING STUDENTS HOW TO HELP EACH OTHER

We've seen that forcing motivated students to pair up with failing students to solve the same problems at the same time and the same pace is generally a disaster, as is grouping random children together to solve problems that might not be at the right level for any child in the group, and that it is much better for students to ask for very specific help from their peers when they need it, and to help others when they genuinely want to.

How can we bring this about and how can we make the experience of children helping each other as productive and rewarding as possible?

The first step is to model taking great joy in sharing mathematical insights and problem-solving techniques and knowledge with others. If you, as the teacher, love doing this, your joy will be contagious. Children are drawn to fun. If you make it fun, they will want to join in, and by fun I do not mean taking the rigor and challenge out of it. I mean showing the children that the process of diving into a hard problem and meeting the challenge is pleasurable and satisfying.

In an orderly and structured environment, children like helping others, as long as that helping is truly valuable. They do not like being used as pawns and having their good nature or their gentleness exploited. Quiet, hard-working children do not like being seated beside a cluster of chatterboxes who won't settle to the task at hand in order to bring some balance to the boisterous group. Motivated math students do not like being asked to "help" failing students with problems far beyond their reach in order to bring up the average grade in the room and make the class appear more functional than it really is.

Children do, however, love giving hints to children who are eager to solve a problem. They love explaining things to others who are really listening. They love helping when that help is of real service.

Teaching children how to teach is a very worthwhile investment of time. It enables them to better help their peers, and it is a valuable skill they will be able to use for the rest of their lives in almost any field they might go into as well as with their own families.

I teach children these principles of good explaining/helping:

1. Make eye contact to establish a connection.
2. Do your best to figure out exactly what the other person is confused by. A person who is stuck wants help on precisely that obstacle, not a general lecture on related topics.
3. Zero in on that area of confusion.
4. In some cases, the most empowering way to help someone is to offer a hint rather than an explanation and then check if the hint is enough to get them unstuck.
5. Whenever you are explaining math to another person, ask questions to make sure the person is following you and is actively listening. (Do not ask questions to expose or embarrass the person). Examples of good questions would be: "What will the next term in this sequence be?" or "Does this make sense now?" or "Is there any part

you're still not sure about?" Poor questions would be: "So you don't get any of this stuff at all?" or "How come you don't know this when you're in fourth grade?"

6. Offer positive feedback.

I teach children to go through these steps when explaining a mathematical procedure such as cubing a number, or finding the surface area of a sphere, to another child who has asked for help:

- Show the student how to do the procedure in the simplest possible way for the simplest case with the smallest numbers that will illustrate the concept. For example, show the student how to find the surface area of a sphere with radius equal to 2. Draw a very simple and straightforward picture as you are demonstrating the procedure so the person can take in the information visually as well as by listening.
- Next, ask the student to do a very similar problem with you, using a slightly larger radius like 3, with you guiding the steps and asking small, manageable questions like, "What does r stand for?" and, "What number should we put for the exponent?" and, "Will you draw the symbol for pi right here?" and, "What does three squared equal?"
- Finally, ask the student to show you how to do the procedure with a slightly larger number such as 5. In this way, check their understanding. If they get stuck, offer the smallest hint or guidance that will enable them to carry on solving the problem rather than jumping in and completing it for them.

I explain to the children that when we are helping someone, we don't want to simply give the person the answer; we want to give her the knowledge or skills to solve the problem and other similar problems on her own. We also want to put the person at ease, partly because this is the respectful and friendly thing to do, and also because people learn math better when they are feeling comfortable.

This style of peer teaching can be taught to the entire class in a guided Socratic style with the teacher eliciting from the children how they think they can best explain things to others and how they themselves most like to be helped.

When I see individual children helping other children, I sometimes kneel down beside their desks so my face is level with theirs and offer teaching tips like, "What could you ask Jerome now to be sure he is understanding you?" or, "As you explain the next step, look into Alejandra's eyes and see if her eyes are conveying understanding."

Children should also be instructed in how to ask for help, not just how to offer it. The teacher can lead a class discussion in which she conveys to the children that asking for very specific help using precise terms generally leads to much better results than nebulous appeals like, "I don't get any of this!" which are hard to respond to helpfully. The teacher can ask the class to come up with examples of specific questions and vague ones so the students clearly understand the difference.

a fifth grader helping younger children with analytic geometry

26

TRAINING CHILDREN TO TEACH FULL-SIZED CLASSES

One year when I was teaching at Malcolm X School in South Berkeley, I decided to train a group of children to teach entire classes. I invited a dozen children to bring their lunches to an empty classroom during the lunch hour. All the students were in the fifth grade, all were from low-income families, and all but two were minorities which are typically under-represented in math-based fields.

Their attendance, I explained to them, would be purely optional, but if they decided they wanted to come, I wanted them to stick with it for a few months. They would be giving up their lunch hour, but in exchange, they would learn how to teach.

The children were delighted with the suggestion. Twice a week they would get their lunches on trays from the cafeteria and rush along the hall to practice their teaching skills.

During our first class, I asked them to think of all the teaching techniques and strategies that had ever seen, and as a group we divided these up into two categories: effective and noneffective. The children came up with an enormous number and felt strongly that certain techniques were far more likely to facilitate learning than others.

This exploration opened them up to the idea that teaching is composed of a long series of choices rather than being something that simply happens automatically — with either good or bad results — when a teacher stands at the front of the room.

Next, I modeled for the children teaching errors such as avoiding eye contact, mumbling, talking to the board instead of to the class, and talking too quickly. The children had to identify each error, explain why it interfered with learning, and demonstrate an improvement on my example.

After this discussion, I had them select the dozen techniques which they considered the most valuable so we could focus on these. We took an algebra topic the children were familiar with from my work with them in their regular classrooms (exponentiation) and I invited each child to the board to teach the rest of the group. The child, before starting to teach, would identify several techniques she planned to make use of, such as asking questions, asking for feedback on fingers, and making eye contact.

After the child had finished teaching, the other children offered comments and suggestions. This critiquing was done in a very structured way. The children understood that its sole purpose was to improve the teaching abilities of everyone in the group and that there was no room for gratuitous criticism.

I gave each child in the room a copy of the algebra text that was being used by the college-track algebra students at Berkeley High School. Many of the topics that the children taught over the coming weeks were selected from this text. The book added to their sense of pride in becoming peer teachers and they carried the books everywhere.

The peer teachers became more and more adept, and after they had practiced long and hard on teaching each other, they moved on to teaching full-sized classes in their school. Several of the peer teachers taught as a team in the classrooms we went to. One would go to the board and teach the algebra signals to the class, then the next would teach the first portion of the lesson on exponents, a third would come to the board to create a logarithm table with the class, and then the child who had introduced the signals would return to the board to lead the class through their first example of multiplying exponential terms.

A ten-year-old experiences the satisfaction of understanding an algebra concept so well he is able to teach it to others.

The children who were being taught — also fifth graders — were spellbound. The peer teachers had spent weeks learning how to command the attention of a group and how to redirect the attention of a child who is daydreaming or talking to a neighbour. Though they told me later that they had been nervous, they spoke in clear, well-projected voices and handled the discipline in a firm and even-handed way.

"Pay attention," ten-year-old Myesha told a boy named Jacob, sensing that his mind was not grappling with the exponents as hard as she wanted it to. Jacob looked up, slightly startled, and after Myesha's two words of advice, his attention never wavered from the math. Interestingly, he did not appear to harbour any resentment over Myesha speaking to him as authoritatively as a stern but loving grandmother.

The peer teachers were able to anticipate behavior problems almost before they manifested themselves and make use of the methods they had learned in order to intervene, preventatively. In one instance a boy named DaRon was attempting to disrupt the peer teachers by feigning disbelief in a mathematical concept. The peer teacher, John, was able to recognize instantly that this "bafflement," rather than being a genuine expression of confusion, was designed to send the class off its rails. John took several steps toward DaRon, looked straight into his eyes, summed up his ploy with calm authority, and then in a friendly voice invited DaRon to give the answer to the next question, conveying his utter confidence in DaRon's understanding. An adult might well have been unable to grasp or resolve this problem so quickly and smoothly.

Some of the peer teachers had been quite renowned troublemakers. I took photographs of them teaching and mounted the photos on a large poster board, in the centre of which were a few challenging algebra problems. Under the problems, I wrote: "Having trouble with these problems? Ask the algebra peer teachers at your school for help." Under each peer teacher's photo was his or her name.

I was in the school office one day getting ready to affix the poster board to the wall just outside the office when a woman I had never seen before came over and looked at it.

"That is not Javonda," she said, looking at Javonda's photo. "Not Javonda Jones."

"Yes," I said. "That's Javonda Jones, one of the algebra peer teachers."

"No, Honey, that is not," she said. "I known Javonda Jones all her life and she not no algebra teacher. She what you call a big pain in the posterior, not no algebra teacher."

I smiled, and then the woman smiled too, conceding that some unexpected change must have taken place, and told me, "I got to mention this to Javonda mother. Now I seen it all."

As she walked away I heard her chuckling to herself with pleasure and repeating, "Now I seen it all!"

A number of the children went through transformations like Javonda did. They were no longer the ones who caused big commotions in the lunchroom or led their classmates into inappropriate laughing spells in class with sarcastic commentaries on their lessons. Instead, they became confident and articulate leaders of academic enthusiasm. They began to appear in the school office not to serve punishments but to report proudly on their latest teaching successes, the high-school textbook prominently on display.

teaching the order of operations

The following year I decided to try training even younger children to teach. At Emerson School, a couple of miles away, I selected a dozen seven-years-olds and invited them to learn how to teach. They were excited and eager to begin. After a few weeks of practicing, the peer teachers taught a full period of math to another second-grade class. Taking turns, they described René Descartes' discovery of the Cartesian plane, taught the class how to find truth and false sets for equations in two variables, showed the class how to graph these sets, and taught the class a number of new words including quadrant, axes, cardinality, and linear. The class they taught was keenly attentive, responding to all their questions and even asking some of their own.

A ten-year-old girl teaches her theory about composite functions to the class.

27

MAKING USE OF THE BRAIN'S PLASTICITY TO DEVELOP STRONG MATH SKILLS

What are the qualities of a strong math student? What does a strong math student do differently from a weak or struggling one when solving a problem?

A strong student makes sense of the problem, sorts the problem by type, breaks it down into more manageable pieces if necessary, and uses the appropriate strategies or procedures to solve each chunk. If the problem seems unfamiliar on its face, the strong student looks more carefully to find similarities between the new problem and problems the student has successfully solved before. A strong student determines when perseverance is needed, and when it is time to ask for help.

A weak student tends to view the problem as one big daunting unfamiliar whole and tries to attack it in a random and chaotic fashion without recognizing what kind of problem is it or breaking it down.

How can we turn weak students into strong ones, and make strong ones even stronger?

Weak students who are left to flail learn to fail. They practice failure every day, and the more they practice it, the better they get at it. Their brains get wired for failure. This is one reason students who are slightly behind in first grade often end up drastically far behind by the time they reach high school.

In the same way that failing students get better and better at failing, successful students tend to get better and better at succeeding. Two children who don't look terribly different mathematically when they are six years old can go through the same school system and even be in the same math classes through middle school, and end up miles apart by eleventh grade, with one acing AP Calculus and the other still not able to borrow when subtracting three-digit numbers.

A good "math brain" can be shaped by directly guiding children to solve math problems efficiently and successfully. A very different sort of "math brain" is created by letting children flounder and thrash around. These struggling children live in a mathematical chaos. When you see children like this trying to solve a math problem, they grope around as if they are in a dark room full of math symbols and snippets of procedures and shards of algorithms, grabbing hold of things that have nothing to do with the problem at hand. The longer they do this groping around in the dark— which creates an enormous sense of frustration and futility and hopelessness that in turn forms a tight association between math symbols and thoughts like, "Oh what's the point? I hate math! I'm so bad at it!" — the more chaotic their inner math landscape becomes. Years of bad math experiences hardwire inefficient thought-paths that sabotage a child's ability to do math.

We need to intervene long, long before children's brains get wired for failure — and if the situation has been allowed to run unchecked so that older students have developed a habit of failing, we need to help them break this habit.

How?

During math class, we need to place the focus on making sure all students have repeated experiences of success. We want them to solve problems efficiently and correctly, over and over and over.

The idea that it is good to let children spend most of math class in states of confusion, vaguely taking stabs at division using four different methods, none of which are mastered or understood, or zoning out while someone else in a group solves the problem of the day and shares the solution, is very misguided. This approach does not build resilience. It does not inspire mathematical curiosity or inventiveness. It does not teach children the value of teamwork. It simply gives children lots and lots of experiences of looking at math problems, becoming overwhelmed, and failing to solve them. Instead, we want to create the circuitry in the brain which makes it easier and easier for children to make sense of problems, dive in, and successfully solve them.

One area of math at which American students score particularly badly is solving multi-step problems. For example, in 2009, the National Assessment of Educational Progress found that only 22% of 8th graders were able to answer this question correctly:

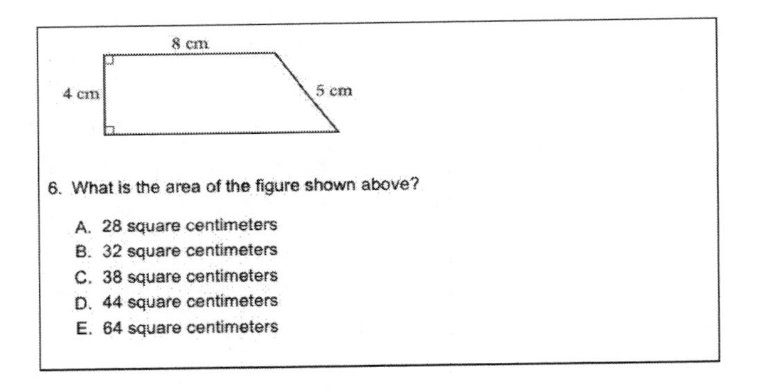

6. What is the area of the figure shown above?

A. 28 square centimeters
B. 32 square centimeters
C. 38 square centimeters
D. 44 square centimeters
E. 64 square centimeters

No doubt most of these young teenagers knew the meaning of the word area and a good many of them knew the Pythagorean Theorem, but they were unable to break the problem down into steps.

These same flummoxed students would probably have been able to maneuver characters on a video screen through perilous situations, making decisions at lightning speed, and press all the right buttons on their handheld controllers without even glancing down at them.

What is the big difference? Practice.

An essential part of making sure children have repeated experiences of problem-solving success is providing the children with math that is at just the right level for them to succeed with and then providing increasingly difficult math at that particular child's learning pace.

Just providing the right level of math is not enough, though. We need to teach children — *directly and explicitly*, and not just with vague hints— how to solve a wide variety of types of problems in mathematically sound and efficient ways. By direct instruction, I do not mean lecturing; most students tune out lectures unless the lectures are very short and tailored to the student's needs and the student has some control over the pace (as is the case with the brief explanatory videos on Khan Academy).

Guided discovery

An excellent way to teach students how to solve a new type of problem they have not encountered before is to start by giving them a version of the problem which has been broken down into small manageable steps and then requiring the children to do each step.

In effect, the students are guided to discover the solution by answering a sequence of questions which were specifically written to make the problem and solution as accessible and transparent as possible. If a child does each step independently and arrives at the solution, she is far more likely to retain this knowledge than if she watched the teacher do each step. If a child gets stuck on a step, she can ask for help.

When the child has fully mastered doing a certain type of problem in this structured and guided way, she can then be offered similar problems in which she is put in charge of partially breaking down the problem, and, when this is mastered, fully breaking down the problem herself.

If she chooses to come up with a different way of correctly solving the problem, this should be praised — but at a bare minimum, every student should be taught one clear and efficient way to solve the kinds of problems which they will repeatedly encounter. Inventiveness on the part of the child is beautiful icing on the cake — but the kind of guided discovery I have just described should be freely offered to all children rather than withheld in favour of having the children struggle for days or weeks with problems they lack the skills to solve.

This experience of repeated success with solving a series of increasingly difficult problems develops the habit of being able to read a problem, make sense of it, break it down, do each step, and arrive at the correct answer. This, in turn, creates confidence and competence.

This method is critically important for older students as well

It is not only young children who learn more and become much stronger math students when they are offered math problems which are completely broken down into steps, then into fewer steps, and finally into no steps. It is *also* the case for older students studying pre-calculus and calculus and other higher-level math classes.

There is a remarkably ill-conceived underlying premise in most algebra, geometry, and calculus textbooks; these textbooks state some facts, show several examples, and then ask the student to jump in and solve complicated problems which depend upon these facts but which are quite dissimilar to the worked examples and require many steps, as well as conceptual leaps, which would not be obvious at all to most students. This often results in students getting hopelessly confused and searching the internet for solutions to the given problems and trying to make sense of them, or giving up entirely and copying other students' work.

The students would have a much better experience, learn more, and enjoy the math more if each problem set in the textbook started with problems in which the steps are broken down to guide the student to the solution, then moved on to problems in which the student must break them down himself, and culminated in more challenging problems which depend upon the skills just learned and which the student must break down entirely on his own.

If textbooks were written in this helpful manner there would be far less need for parents to hire tutors to show students how to do this. It is a much more efficient and far less painful way to learn math. The sink or swim method used in most textbooks might build great resilience in a few students, but for most — particularly when the student reaches algebra and pre-calculus — it either hopelessly confuses them or turns a manageable concept into a long drawn-out ordeal.

The point of a math book should be to introduce students to new concepts, develop and deepen their understanding, and make them more independent, rather than making them feel they cannot progress without constantly asking for help or having a private tutor. In addition, the necessity for lots of help widens the divide between students whose parents did not master algebra and calculus and lack the resources to hire private tutors and those students whose parents are very skilled at math and/or can pay for tutors.

There is a place for hard problems with non-obvious solutions, but students are far more likely to succeed with these problems if they have been explicitly taught, both by the teacher and by working through well-written problem sets, to break down multi-step problems.

~

Many years ago, back in the 1980's, I saw a set of photographs in a magazine which I never forgot. They were MRIs which showed the brain activity of a high-IQ person trying to solve a certain problem and the brain activity of a low IQ person trying to solve the same problem.

The high-IQ person's brain lit up in a specific place. The low-IQ person's brain lit up all over the place.

This research fascinated me because I sensed it held a key to turning poor math students into good ones. Long before brain plasticity became a popular topic, I was convinced that a child's ability to do things that required intelligence — such as math — was not fixed or pre-determined. Trying to change a child's IQ seemed like a very difficult challenge, in part because I was not convinced that an IQ test would give a fair measure of the intelligence of many of the children in my classes. Over and over, I had seen children who had been deemed slow and who had a history of academic failure make what appeared to be quantum leaps in intelligence when they were taught and treated differently.

When I saw the starkly contrasting MRIs, I asked myself: how can we take a child whose brain appears to be firing chaotically all over the place and turn that child into one whose brain fires efficiently in the right places when he is trying to solve math problems? Whether this change shows up on an IQ test later or not, this will make the child functionally much more intelligent, which is what really matters.

I have always felt confident that the way to do this is to teach a child — by direct, carefully guided, step-by-step instruction — to solve problems in the most efficient manner and then require the child to solve many, many very similar problems increasingly independently, and then solve problems which are the same at their core but look different on the surface or are embedded in other problems. In this way, we train the child's brain to "light up" in the right places.

There are child geniuses whose talents seem far out of proportion to the instruction they are given, and there are children who have suffered brain damage which makes math incredibly difficult for them — but in between these two extremes, there are millions and millions of children whose math capabilities can be significantly increased with the kind of clear and guided instruction which maximizes the child's engagement with sequences of questions which lead the child to deep understanding.

28

THE ROLE OF MEMORIZATION IN LEARNING MATH

There is a great deal of confusion and debate in math education surrounding memorization. Those opposed like to argue that if a child memorizes math, she will fail to understand it conceptually and won't be able to apply the memorized math if the problem appears in a different form. Opponents of memorization also claim that forced memorization of math facts can lead to trauma and lasting math anxiety. Those in favour of memorization sometimes go overboard and want children to memorize all manner of things that are not suited to memorization.

A distinction needs to be made between the two main categories of math that can be memorized. The first category includes math facts like 7 x 8, algorithms such as the set of rules one would use to multiply a pair of two-digit numbers, and facts such as the sum of the angles of a triangle totaling 180 degrees.

The second category of math involves the *application* of all these sorts of things — for example, solving a problem like "Find the sum of the angles of a hexagon."

The first category should be memorized. The second category should not be. In fact, if a child is attempting to memorize how to find the sum of the angles of a hexagon before a test, this should be a warning sign to the teacher and parents that the child does not conceptually understand the math involved and needs to back up and focus on deeply understanding the math rather than investing time in memorizing. The impulse to memorize, in this case, would be an indication of confusion or very superficial understanding in the student.

Why memorize math facts and basic algorithms?

The biggest reason to require children to memorize arithmetic facts is to increase the children's enjoyment of math and their chances of mastering increasingly difficult topics. If you had to read a three-hundred-page novel by sounding out every letter, this would very quickly kill your pleasure in the story. You would certainly not want to repeat the experience. Children who try to learn multi-digit multiplication or division or certain parts of algebra before they have memorized their times tables are slowed down to the point that math becomes a tedious ordeal they want to get away from. Not having memorized their math facts is a very significant handicap.

Learning to read is not always easy. For some children, it is extremely difficult and takes a long time. Nevertheless, it is worth it. Memorizing math facts is similar. The argument that this is an outdated skill now that we have calculators is absurd. We also have computer programs which will turn text into sound — but imagine if you had to input every written word you encountered into such a program. This would limit your freedom considerably.

Just as being able to read fluently frees up a person's brain to contemplate the ideas in the writing rather than having the brain engaged in laboriously trying to decode individual words and remember previously decoded words in the same sentence, being fluent with math facts allows a person to focus on ideas and concepts rather than falling into time-consuming and tiring attempts to deal with arithmetic operations by counting on fingers or making little tally marks on a page.

Addition facts

Before there is any deliberate attempt to memorize addition facts, a child should clearly understand what addition means. A child should be completely at ease with addition and able to solve any simple addition problem independently before being asked to memorize anything related to addition.

The best way I have ever found to teach addition is with Cuisenaire rods. These are coloured wooden rods of varying sizes. Basic Cuisenaire rods come in lengths of one centimeter through ten centimeters.

When children learn arithmetic with Cuisenaire rods, they learn about the relative sizes of numbers and the relationship between numbers. The rods are a perfect size for small hands and a perfect size for desktops. The children can see and feel that six is bigger than five, that two threes is the same as six, that ten is the same as ten ones, and twenty is two tens. Working with the rods, children develop a deep understanding of concepts like even and odd and divisibility at the same time as they are learning to add and multiply.

Before memorizing addition facts, children should reach the point where they can look at any addition problem on paper (using numbers up to 10) and make a model of it using Cuisenaire rods and state the answer. They should also be able to look at any pair of end-to-end rods and say and write down what addition problem the rods represent. Memorizing addition facts prior to this level of conceptual understanding is pointless.

The addition facts which should be memorized are: adding any two one-digit numbers and adding any number up to twenty to any one-digit number. For example, a child should be able to answer questions like 9 + 8 or 17 + 4 instantly without doing any counting or calculating. Subtraction should be taught in the same manner — conceptual understanding first, then memorizing the facts.

Multiplication facts

Cuisenaire rods are also the perfect tool for teaching multiplication. The children should be taught that 4 x 2 can be solved by taking four of the 2 cm rods and lining them up end to end and then finding a single rod that matches this length exactly. This should be practiced until the children can easily create a model for any simple multiplication problem. 5 x 2 is five 2 cm rods. 2 x 3 is two 3 cm rods. As they practice this they will develop a feel for what 5 x 2 really means. It will become apparent to them, without anyone mentioning the term "commutative" or asking them to memorize that a x b = b x a, that 2 x 5 (two 5 cm rods) is the same length as 5 x 2 (five 2-cm rods).

Just like with addition, prior to memorizing any times tables, the child should understand exactly what multiplication means. A child should be able to look at an end-to-end arrangement of rods (such as four 3 cm rods) and say and write what multiplication problem it represents.

Questions should be phrased in the most accessible way. Asking, "What multiplication problems does this model represent?" is a very poor choice of words if one is talking to a six or seven-year-old. A better phrasing would be, "These rods show 5 x 3." (Pointing to five 3 cm rods arranged end to end.) "What do these rods show?" (Pointing to a different arrangement of rods.)

When children can go back and forth easily between a multiplication problem and a tangible model (Cuisenaire rods being the ideal example) and are beginning to say the answers without having to figure them out (for example, they line up four fives and immediately reach for two 10 rods to show the answer is twenty or even quickly say twenty as soon as they have lined up the fives), they are ready to start memorizing.

Children should memorize all the times table up to 12 x 12, meaning they should be able to answer questions like 9 x 7 or 12 x 6 without doing any kind of calculation.

Short regular bursts of memorizing

The memorizing of math facts should be done in the most efficient manner possible. If it is done inefficiently, children in grade six will still be making halfhearted but time-consuming stabs at memorizing math facts, all the while taking ten times as long to do the rest of their math work.

A child should not spend more than ten minutes a day (broken into two five-minute bursts) memorizing unless the child really wants to go on for longer. Pressing a child to spend half an hour memorizing, against his will, is counterproductive — but the two short daily bursts must be done at least five days a week, without fail, until the memorization has been completed.

A peer who knows the facts or an adult should point to an array and have the child state the fact that matches it, followed by pointing to the commuted version. ("Four times six is twenty-four. Six times four is twenty-four.") If the child is not sure of a fact, the person who knows it should state it and have the child repeat it while the child touches the corresponding array. Looking at the visual model while saying the fact aloud will help many children retain the information.

For a detailed set of instructions for how to help children memorize their multiplication tables, please visit my website janemolnar.com and see the section on "Helping Children Memorize Multiplication Tables".

Memorization takes time

Barring a serious brain injury or another very significant issue, all children are capable of memorizing math facts. The main impediment is not that the child "is bad at math" or "inherited the parent's inability to memorize" or "has ADHD" or "is a right-brained child." The main reason children fail to memorize math facts is that they do not put in the necessary time. Some people think that if a child spends a few minutes now and then trying to memorize something and fails to memorize it, then the child is not up to the task when really all that happened was the child was allowed to give up.

Different children learn different things at widely varying rates. Some children learn to read fluently with almost no instruction at age five while others need years of direct instruction to reach that same level. Some children can memorize facts swiftly and apparently effortlessly while other children need to work away at the same task over a period of weeks or months. Nevertheless, to be successful in math, children need to memorize math facts and master algorithms to the point of automaticity.

Dragging out this memorization over a period of five or ten years, as is quite common these days, makes the task more painful, not less. It's best to simply take the time to do it in the early elementary years, generally somewhere between the ages of about six and nine.

Memorization is often seen as a waste of valuable class time. This is a mistake. For one thing, learning how to memorize is a valuable skill which should be taught explicitly rather than left to chance. Also, assigning the entire task of memorizing math facts as homework can backfire. Some families will take on the job and others won't and this will create an unnecessary divide in the classroom. The successful memorization of math facts and the learning of techniques for memorizing are so important that five minutes a day of class time should be devoted to this during stages of math development when memorization is critical. Inevitably, some students will accomplish the task long before the rest of the class and should, of course, be allowed to get on with other work.

Do not pair math and stress

Though I am a firm believer in children memorizing math facts, I feel equally strongly that no part of this memorization should include shame or anxiety. Children should be told that they need to memorize a clearly defined set of facts and that everyone's brain is unique; some brains memorize quickly but take longer to solve problems, while other brains take longer to commit facts to memory but solve problems very fast. Yet other brains make take a long time both to memorize facts and to solve problems yet may come up with novel ways of solving problems, or retain mastered material longer than a brain that took it in with speed and ease.

In some classes, children are required to do a page of arithmetic problems rapidly before a timer rings. In other classes, children are called on in quick succession to answer multiplication problems in front of the whole class. These methods of memorization cause some children unnecessary stress and worry and create an unproductive and artificial hierarchy of "winners" and "losers".

The point of memorizing math facts is not to establish superiority over others and it is not necessary to be able to write down answers at breakneck speed. The real point of memorizing is to be able to free up the brain to focus on the more challenging parts of a problem rather than on computation, to develop more agility and competence and see the bigger picture, and to be able to accomplish tasks efficiently such as calculating a tip or comparing two products in the grocery store or making sense of a home mortgage or a car loan. None of these things need to be done so quickly that one feels manic while doing the calculation. The goal is ease and empowerment, not mania.

Children who are able to memorize swiftly and who have great manual dexterity with their pencils will likely feel smart and pleased at being able to write down the answers to fifty problems in a minute — but children for whom memorization does not come so easily or whose memory retrieval is accurate but slower, or whose hand dexterity is not so developed, can soon become anxious in an environment that places a high value on extreme speed. If there is one thing that does not spur on math mastery, it is anxiety. Anxiety overwhelms and freezes children, and it tends to snowball. It is not a good motivator. It interferes with both the desire to do math and the capacity to learn.

A far better way to approach this is to tell the children they will need to memorize a set of facts and that it may happen quickly or it may happen slowly, but the important thing is that they all succeed. Success does not mean that all thirty children in a class will be able to say the answer to 9 x 8 in less than a second. There is a huge range in retrieval speed in different children. A child with a slower memory retrieval speed might take five seconds to answer a question that another child might respond to in a fraction of a second. This does not mean the first child has failed to memorize the times tables, and nor does it mean that this child will not be successful in math. Tiny lags of seconds (which can make a huge difference during a timed test of fifty problems and cause acute anxiety) do not interfere with children successfully solving problems.

Algorithms

Basic arithmetic algorithms should also be memorized, meaning that children should be shown how to do them and required to practice until the procedures become automatic. As with math facts, understanding of the operation should come first. For example, before memorizing the algorithm for division, a child should understand what division means and be able to show, with small objects or by drawing a model, how to solve problems like $27 \div 3$ or $30 \div 6$. If they are unable to do this, they are not ready to memorize the algorithm and need to spend more time solving simple division problems using Cuisenaire rods or small objects like beans or by drawing.

When a child has a basic understanding of what an operation means and can swiftly and accurately solve problems (using numbers that are not cumbersomely large) without using an algorithm, she is ready to learn the applicable algorithm.

This is where things often fall apart in the classroom, in one of two ways. The first potential disaster is requiring the children to discover their own algorithms. This almost always leads to wasted time and confusion. While young children are fully capable of certain types of mathematical abstraction, they are highly unlikely to come up with an efficient algorithm for dividing multi-digit numbers, or for dividing fractions.

The second place where things tend to go very wrong in the teaching of arithmetic lies in the withholding of basic algorithms under the theory that if the children cannot fully explain every step of the algorithm, they should not be using it.

Young children can learn and use algorithms with confidence and accuracy long before they are able to justify every aspect of the algorithm. A nine-year-old, for example, can learn the algorithm for short division, or for multiplying or dividing fractions, yet would likely have difficulty explaining the reasoning behind every step. This does not mean that the algorithm should be kept from the child. However much some educators might like to pretend otherwise, it is a handicap in life not to be able to manipulate numbers with ease.

There are all sorts of things we teach children which enrich their lives even though they might not be able to provide a deep explanation of exactly why the process works. We teach children to ride bicycles without requiring them to design the gear system or explain the physics of balance first. We teach them to cook without insisting they must begin by discovering or explaining the chemistry of a cake rising.

Sometimes it is best to learn a skill and be able to make use of it with ease and accuracy and explore the precise nature of why it works later. This is certainly the case with the algorithms for numerical operations.

Keep the primary focus on more interesting math

While this memorizing is taking place in the early elementary grades, the majority of the child's daily math time should be devoted to fun and interesting problem-solving of a sort that does not depend heavily on the math facts already having been memorized. The number one goal should be to have the children take joy in learning math and love it. In sharp contrast to anxiety which tends to shut down learning, joy is both relaxing and stimulating. It motivates children to go further and deeper, to persist with challenging problems, to want to return to math as soon as possible.

29

EXPLAIN YOUR ANSWER ON PAPER: HOW TO TURN CHILDREN AGAINST MATH

If someone were to give me the unlikely assignment of taking a class of thirty children and trying to frustrate and annoy them, ruin their experience of math, and slow down their learning tremendously, I would know exactly how to go about it.

I would assign a set of math problems (the same problems for all the children, regardless of their level of proficiency and speed) and tell the children they needed to explain on paper exactly how they arrived at their answers, using full sentences.

Most children hate doing this.

Why do children, including ones who love to write, recoil from explaining on paper where their math answers came from?

Their resistance to explaining their mathematical reasoning on paper is completely different from their resistance to a rather dry task like memorizing times tables. Most children will not take the initiative in memorizing math facts and would prefer to do something else, yet they can understand that it is useful to have their math facts memorized. If pressed to memorize them, children will, and after they have, they will be glad they did. I have never met anyone of any age who memorized the times tables and later wished they had not bothered.

Children generally loathe explaining mathematical processes on paper because it distracts them from learning and doing math. It's not a simple matter of finding it tedious. Their resistance runs deeper than that, and forcing them to explain their reasoning on paper comes with a price.

Show Your Work Versus Explain How You Got Your Answer

A clear distinction needs to be made between asking children to show their work or show the steps of a formal procedure and asking them to explain where their answers came from. It is perfectly reasonable to ask a child to show her work, meaning that she must solve a math problem or set of problems on one page rather than using a separate piece of scratch paper to solve parts of the problems and then writing the final answers on the page she will hand in and discarding the scratch paper.

If a child does her computations or diagrams on a piece of paper that the teacher does not get to see, it is harder to pin down where the child went wrong if she arrives at a wrong answer. She might have understood exactly how to solve the problem but made a small arithmetic error — or she might have had no idea how to solve the problem and put down a guess.

Seeing the written steps a child took, all in one place, is useful for both the child and the teacher. It gives the teacher more insight into the child's level of understanding and also allows the child to check her work more easily and find her errors and correct them.

It is also reasonable — at the right stage — to ask a child who is learning a new procedure to write down each step in a formal way. For example, if a child is working on $6x + 5 = 29$, even though the child might be able to solve this problem in his head, it would be reasonable, at the right time, to ask him to show the steps of subtracting five from both sides and then dividing both sides by 6. This encourages the child to solve the problem in a systematic way which in turn makes it easier to solve similar problems involving bigger numbers, and to solve more complicated equations which have more steps. Following precise steps also tends to result in more consistently correct answers. Teaching children how to construct formal proofs (again, at the right stage) is also a very valuable skill.

On the other hand, insisting that a child explain on paper how he arrived at his answer after he has solved a problem, or making him explain his steps in sentences as he works on a problem, is far from helpful.

Requiring a child to explain his answers is rather like insisting that a child in an art class explain (in writing) his painting. If you give a class of children a stack of thick watercolor paper and some good watercolour paints and invite them to paint, they will be happy. You could show them techniques and set up a big table with art books they could look through for inspiration. You could invite them to set up arrangements of objects and paint a still life. They will develop their painting skills and all will be well. The more they paint and look at other people's paintings and are shown specific techniques like how to draw a nose or how to create shadows and then practice these skills, the better they will get.

But suppose every time a child does a painting, you require him to write a paragraph explaining how he arrived at the painting. Very quickly, most children will lose momentum.

"But this is my painting. What do you mean explain it?"

"Well, explain why you added purple over in this corner. And why this dark patch here?"

"That's just how it felt right. Can I just write that I painted what felt right?"

"No, no. I want you to write a full paragraph *explaining your process*."

"Can I do another painting now and explain them both later?"

"No. You're not allowed to take another piece of paper until you have explained your artistic process. How did you arrive at this painting?"

"I just painted it. And now I really want to try a still life using the apple and the olive oil bottle and the key. I want to try that shadowing you showed us ..."

"All in good time. I'll keep your next piece of paper here and you can have it when you have written your explanation of that first painting."

"I don't really know what you mean but I'll try ..."

The child writes:

> *I decided to paint a picture because I wanted to. I picked colors I like. I put a purple blotch in the corner because it seemed like a good place for a purple blotch. I painted a chair in the middle because I thought of that. I made the chair green because green chairs are nice.*

This explanation does not give the child any real insight into his art. It adds nothing. He created his painting by sinking into the activity of painting. Rather than helping him paint an even better picture next time, or understand his art or himself more deeply, the whole exercise of forcing a child to try to turn a nonverbal process into a verbal one feels awkward and contrived. If repeated over and over, it starts to form a barrier in the child's mind between his urge to paint and his actually painting. The unpleasant thought of all the awkward explaining will loom up when he thinks of painting.

Furthermore, he can't put his finger on why this thing the teacher keeps asking for feels all wrong. He knows writing is a legitimate thing, and he knows he is supposed to be able to reflect on things and learn to write better. After all, this is school and it's not as if his teacher is asking him to turn his new painting into a doormat or tear it into strips to line the class hamster's cage. On the surface, the teacher appears to be making a perfectly reasonable request —

yet it feels completely wrong to the child in a way he cannot articulate to himself, let alone to the teacher.

The same analogy could be made about learning to play the piano. Suppose a child, each time he plays a piece — either at home or for the teacher — has to write a reflective paragraph on how he played it. How did he get his fingers to scale that octave? Through what process did his brain take in the notes and direct his fingers to play them? How and why did he remember to play the F sharp?

There would be no problem if the child were taught music theory in addition to learning to play pieces and was asked to answer questions on paper such as, "Draw a quarter note," or, "Circle the arpeggios."

The problem arises when the child is made to switch gears constantly from playing music to writing about the process of playing and explaining or defending how his brain is making sense of the sheets of music. The truth is, he probably doesn't know. The fact that he cannot provide a clear explanation for how his brain makes sense of a sheet of music and directs his hands to play it does not mean he is failing to learn the piano or is learning in a superficial and sub-par manner.

A child who is very accomplished at painting or very talented at the piano or excelling in math is no more likely to want to explain the process on paper than a child who is struggling with these skills. The resistance in the child does not arise from ineptitude or confusion or laziness.

The resistance arises because it is distracting and jarring to jump back and forth between the task of solving a problem and the task of explaining how one's brain is solving the problem. It interferes with the natural flow and momentum of the process.

Over the last forty years I have taught hundreds of children and closely observed what helps and what hinders their mathematical development. I have arrived at the conclusion that demanding that children explain their mathematical reasoning on paper undermines their mathematical development rather than supports it.

There is a state of ease a person can enter when completely absorbed in an activity like writing or doing math or playing an instrument or painting or drawing or teaching. In this state, which is typically highly pleasurable, we forget about time, worries, and almost anything but what we are working on.

***This* is the state we want children to enter when they are doing math: a state that is happy, peaceful, focused, deeply absorbed, and productive.**

As teachers, we need to do everything we can to create the right environment and the right kind of assignments to increase the chances that children will fall into this state and stay in it for prolonged periods.

A key element of this state is focus. We need to set up the classroom in a way that is conducive to focus, and then allow children to sink into an activity.

Do not fragment a child's focus

A math problem may be stated in words but when we ask children to solve it, we need to allow the children the freedom to enter into the realm of math and stay there while working instead of demanding that they keep coming back into the realm of English sentences (or whatever their language is).

The unravelling of a math problem, the sifting and the sorting, the recognition of similarities, the leaps, the falling back on familiar algorithms and memorized facts to deal with certain aspects of the problem so the brain can focus on the real core of the matter, the clarity that can come very suddenly ... this is not primarily a verbal process. Words certainly come into it. A person solving a math problem may shift back and forth between thinking in clearly identifiable sentences or sentence fragments and thinking in a way that is precise and accurate but not verbal.

Math as its own language

In math, symbols and pictures hold information which the brain can make sense of without translating them into words. In this sense, math is like a language.

The last thing we want to do when a child is creating a neural pathway for, say, solving a set of two equations in two unknowns, is to fragment the path and add in little detours. We need to allow the child's brain to work smoothly and efficiently. If I see a child struggling, then of course I will offer to help him and will need to use words — but if I see a child happily and productively working on a problem, the last thing I would want to do would be to interfere and break his focus.

Consider, for example, a simple equation like $2b + 5 = 11$. If a person is just learning to make sense of these symbols, they may translate the problem into a sentence in their mind. But when one is proficient in this type of problem, no sentence forms in the mind that says, "Hmmm, two b's plus five is eleven … so the two b's must equal six … and one b must be three." If I were trying to teach the problem to someone else, I would put my finger over the 2b, obscuring the part of the problem that is likely the stumbling part for the child, and ask, "What plus five is eleven?" Naturally, one reaches for language when trying to explain something, but if I were solving the problem by myself I would simply look at it and understand the symbols without translating them into English sentences and then write down the answer.

When a child is becoming fluent in a second language, we want them to connect the new word directly with what it represents, not circle it back to their original language first. If we were trying to get a young English-speaking child to learn the French word "chien", ideally we would connect the new word chien to a picture of a dog or to a real dog if one were handy, not to the English word dog. Yes, we want the child to know that chien means dog — but when the child is conversing in French we do not want him to have to turn every French word he hears into an English word, think of an answer in English, and then translate his response word by word into French, finally answering the other person. We want the child to have a direct experience in French.

In the same way, we need to allow math to be its own language and not force a constant translation into English (or Spanish, etc) on the part of the child.

Encouraging children to experience the beauty of math

If we were to say to a child, "Paint a portrait of someone you love," we would not demand accountability, on the page, for every nuance of colour or texture, or the decision to paint a deep blue background. Once the child enters "painting mode", we let her remain there rather than dragging her back, over and over, across the threshold of language. And we certainly would not deem the painting incomplete until we had forced the child to scrawl words all over her painting explaining how and why she had painted it. We recognize the painting as an object of beauty and meaning *in its own right.*

That's exactly what we should be doing when children are solving math problems. We need to let children go into the realm of math and peacefully work there, coming back on their own time, not artificially hauling them in based on an unproven educational theory that altering their thought process in an unnatural way will help them learn.

The child's mathematical workings, if the child has successfully solved the problem, should be allowed to rest on the page as something aesthetically pleasing in its own right without our insisting the child lard the work with unnecessary sentences of "process" explanation.

If the child has solved the problem correctly and any steps that have been shown are mathematically sound and true, we need to let the math remain just as it is and let the child savour the victory or pleasure of having solved the problem.

If the child has solved the problem incorrectly, we need to isolate the error, acknowledge what the child has done right, and draw the child's attention to the mistake— but in a respectful and helpful manner, not slashing away at their work with broad strokes of a red pen and certainly not demanding they write down how they arrived at the incorrect answer.

Children should be encouraged to see the beauty in math and to create beauty. It is highly unlikely that a child will develop a brand-new proof and this should not be the standard for beauty. A six-year-old, solving a problem in a way that is aesthetically pleasing to her on the page, is creating beauty and this beauty, no matter how simple it might seem to an adult who may have lost their sense of wonder about numbers and patterns and shapes, should be appreciated and respected.

Trying to force a nonverbal process into a verbal one is not helpful. It is distracting, frustrating, and impeding. It wastes valuable time and robs children of experiencing the joy and elegance and flow of math. We want children to know this joy, partly for its own sake but also because joy is the ultimate motivator in math. Grades and rewards and parental expectations and threats of not getting into a good college can never spur on a child as much as a deep love of learning and an intimate familiarity with the beauty and precision and power of a subject.

~

The false dichotomy of rote learning versus deep conceptual understanding

One excuse that is commonly given for demanding that children explain how they got an answer is to reveal whether the child actually understands what he is doing or is just doing it "by rote". Doing something "by rote", when it is mentioned in this context, is considered to be a bad thing.

Let's examine this. First of all, being able to consistently come up with the right answer to a class of problems, even if one could not give a lecture on exactly why this works, is actually an accomplishment, not a failure. If I can safely drive my car to all the places I need to go every day and understand and respect the rules of the road, the fact that I cannot explain how a carburetor works is not a great failing. It's a separate matter. If a person can look at her bill in a restaurant and calculate a 15% tip within a few seconds, this is a valuable skill even if the person could not provide a deep explanation for why her method worked.

A child who can add, subtract, multiply and divide fractions but cannot explain why you invert and multiply the second fraction when dividing has still mastered something very useful and this is not something for us to dismiss as, "Oh sure, he got 100%, but does he know what it all means?"

We need to make a distinction between the valuable skill of being able to execute a procedure with speed and accuracy and the higher-level skill of understanding exactly why this procedure works and being able to articulate this.

When a child is learning a new skill, we want her attention fully on mastering it. If we were teaching a child to ride a bike, we would not stop her every few seconds to get her to explain why she didn't just fall over. The actual experience of learning to ride a bike is a rich and valuable thing in and of itself. The child will soon become fully aware that she needs to go a bit faster in order to keep the bike balanced without being able to explain the physics of this.

Arithmetic is rather like this. The more a child does it, the better she gets at it and the more intuitive sense she develops about it, even if she cannot put this into words yet. Deep conceptual understanding is something that grows as one does increasingly difficult problems and matures.

One way to gauge if the time is right for it is to see if the child spontaneously starts to generalize principles and is eager to engage in a discussion of how and why a concept works. If the child is obviously still wanting to do the problems without explaining them, then the time is not ripe. If a second grader is perfectly willing to do subtraction problems, either on paper or using Cuisenaire rods, but balks at the request to explain what he is doing, he should be allowed to get on with his work in peace.

If I wanted to measure the depth of a child's understanding, there are far better ways to measure this than asking a student to write full sentences explaining how she arrived at an answer.

Suppose, for example, I wanted to know if a group of eight-year-olds understood the concept of place value. I would offer a series of questions (on paper) like this:

Circle the tens digit in 457.
Put a square around the ones digit in 6738.
Underline the hundreds digit in 7469.

How many digits does 326 have?
How many digits does 36,271 have?

Arrange these numbers from smallest to largest: 724 274 472 742 247 427

What is the largest number you can make using the digits 1, 5, and 2?
What is the smallest number you can make using the same digits?

How many tens are needed to make 100?
Write three different numbers which have the same thousands digit.

Give an example of a pair of 2-digit numbers which add up to a 3 digit number:
__ __ + __ __ = __ __ __
Give an example of a pair of 2-digit numbers which add up to a 2 digit number:
__ __ + __ __ = __ __
Is it possible to find a pair of 2-digit numbers which add up to a 4 digit number?
__ __ + __ __ = __ __ __ __

These questions actively engage the child in doing math and thinking about place value. Asking a child to answer a variety of kinds of questions and getting the child to make use of the concept to figure something out is a much better way to gauge his understanding than making him explain it in words on paper. Also, children like answering these kinds of questions and so the measuring of their understanding does not come with the price of creating resistance and boredom in the child.

A child's answers to the questions listed above would give me a far more accurate sense of a child's understanding of place value than a question like:

Simon has three hundred and fifty-two marbles. Mary has four hundred and six marbles. Describe the math situation and show how to arrive at the total number of marbles using a place value math picture. How do you know your answer is correct? Explain.

A child's response to this overly-wordy question which demands still more words is going to give far less precise information about her level of understanding. The question will also likely annoy the child because there is something contrived and artificial about it which the child will quickly sense. It's a question with an agenda, rather than a question designed to let a child get on with enjoying and learning math. Children heartily dislike this sort of math problem.

Frustration, boredom, and resistance are all deterrents to learning. We want children to spend as much time as possible cheerfully doing math and as little time as possible thinking, "Oh not *this* again!"

I can't recall ever encountering a child who wanted to write sentences explaining her math process but if I were to meet such a child, I wouldn't dream of discouraging her. If this method was helping the child, I would welcome it (for that child). I would not, however, impose it on hundreds of other children for whom it was not helpful.

30

AN EXAMPLE OF "EXPLAIN YOUR WORK" RUNNING AMOK

When my youngest son was nine, he spent four months in a fourth-grade public school classroom. Every day in math class the children were told to do a certain page or two in the math workbook. My son would very swiftly write down the answers, show no work, and get them all correct. One day the teacher approached him and asked him where he was getting his answers. "My brain," my son replied. He was told firmly to show his thought process on the page.

The next day in class another page was assigned. As usual, my son read each question quickly and put in the answers. Though about an hour was provided for the class to do the work, this took him four or five minutes, after which he was forbidden to turn the page and carry on because this would have put him out of synch with the rest of the class. He was already badly out of synch; he told me he had learned the concepts in the book when he was in kindergarten — not from me, but from his brother who had cheerfully taken on the role of being his math teacher that year, using Singapore math workbooks.

The teacher again raised the topic with him of his explaining his thinking on paper. At home, he described this to me. "The teacher keeps trying to get me to write down how I figured out the answer but the questions are so easy that I don't have to figure out the answers. They are just obvious! It's like the teacher is trying to get me to explain why two plus two is four. Why is it four? That's just how we named those numbers. Four could have been called five but it wasn't. How am I supposed to explain that to him? And why should I have to explain it? Why can't I just do the math? And why do I have to do kindergarten math?"

Further attempts were made by the teacher to get my son to explain his thinking. My son maintained the position that the questions were too easy to require any thought process. If, for example, he was asked to shade in one-third of a circle, he would simply shade a third and say he did not use any kind of strategy to figure out how to do this; he knew what a third was and did what he was told.

"The teacher is not asking me to explain to someone else how to solve the problems," he told me. "If someone in my group asks for help, I always explain to them how to do it. But that's not what he's trying to get me to write down. He's asking me how *I* got the answer. When I look at the questions, the answers just pop into my head. *That's* how I get them. It's like he's asking me to pretend that I had to figure it out. I didn't need to figure it out. What would you do if someone asked you how you figured out that this word here is "math"? You didn't figure it out, right? You just looked at the word and knew what it was."

When my son got his report card, he had an F in mathematical reasoning — yet he had a deep understanding of both arithmetic and beginning algebra and geometry. Not only did he understand the fourth-grade concepts and do all the in-class work correctly, he consistently scored very highly on all the math tests, and swiftly did his homework every night with no help and got all the questions right.

When my son looked at his report card, he turned pale. For the last few years he had relished math and in addition to working his way through a number of Singapore books, he had spent years doing an online gifted math program through Stanford, worked thousands of problems on Khan Academy, and solved hundreds of the problems I had designed for my students when I was teaching my after-school classes. From babyhood, he had been playing with math puzzles and games. He looked at his F and I saw a shadow fall across his face.

I went and met with the teacher and asked him why he had failed my son in mathematical reasoning. Because I had been teaching my son math since he was tiny, I knew his math reasoning skills were exceptionally strong. A couple of years earlier, when he was seven, I had given him, for the first time and without any explanation of how to do it, a system of equations in two unknowns and asked him to solve it. The equations were $x + y = 17$ and $x - y = 5$. My son looked at the equations on the small sheet of paper, paused briefly and said, "x is 11 and y is 6." When I asked him how he had done it, he reached for some little Lego bricks which happened to be beside us to show me what he had just done in his head. He counted out seventeen bricks and put them in a pile in front of him. From these seventeen, he set aside five to his right, then divided the remaining group on the left in half. He took one of these halves and added it back into the group on the right. He pointed to the group on the left and said, "x is eleven," and then to the group on the right and said, 'y is five." Then he explained that you could use this method to solve any pair of equations of the same type ($x + y = n$ and $x - y = m$ where n and m are positive integers) and the pile on the left would always be x and the pile on the right would be y. I was startled by this demonstration, never having seen anyone solve a set of simultaneous equations in this manner.

"I failed him because he has no idea where his answers are coming from," the teacher explained to me. "He doesn't know what he's doing." Had I not been quite familiar with my son's mathematical insights and clearly articulated reasoning, I might have been quite alarmed.

"Is there any evidence of this?" I asked. "How did he do on the district assessment?" I knew there had been an assessment because my son had told me that several hours of class time had been devoted to it. He had done the whole test in fifteen minutes and then had to sit and wait for two hours and forty-five minutes.

Reluctantly, the teacher looked up my son's score which turned out to be 94%.

"How could he have solved almost all the questions correctly without knowing how to get the answers?" I asked. "That seems highly improbable."

The teacher held to his position that my son, though able to perform well on math tests, was a dismal failure at mathematical reasoning. I was reminded of the famous horse Clever Hans who could correctly stamp out answers to math questions with his hoof without a clue as to what the questions meant, though I kept this image to myself.

I knew that what had actually happened was that my son had internalized the "fourth-grade" topics, long before he reached fourth grade, to a degree that the processes involved had become automatic. The fact that he could shade a third of a circle without having to come up with a special strategy or plan did not mean he did not understand fractions or that he had a severely impaired capacity to reason mathematically. If he had been given a more complicated fraction question like "Darius has $100. He puts 3/4 of this in the bank and then spends 2/5 of the remaining money on a gift for his brother. How much did the gift cost?" he would have had to use reasoning to figure it out and would have been able to draw a sketch and explain his reasoning.

Shortly after my son failed fourth-grade math reasoning, I pulled him out of the public school. He was so relieved to be allowed to learn math at his own pace again that he completed eleven math books during the last two months of the school year, cheerfully reasoning his way through the problems whenever reasoning was required.

31

THE BEST MATH BACKGROUND FOR AN ELEMENTARY MATH TEACHER

Ideally, an elementary-level math teacher should love math and be highly skilled in conveying math concepts, have excellent classroom management skills, and should have earned A's in Algebra 1 and 2, geometry, and pre-calculus, and then done very well in university-level calculus, number theory, abstract algebra, and geometry.

In teaching math to young children, it helps tremendously to have studied math deeply and extensively to a level far beyond that of the students. This provides the teacher with an overview. It allows the teacher to understand where the math topics that the children are working on fit into the larger picture. It provides the teacher with a deep understanding of the significance (or lack of significance) of a child grasping a particular concept in a particular sequence. It helps the teacher predict where the child will likely stumble, further down the road, if a certain concept is not mastered. It enables the teacher to approach a topic from a different angle or possibly delay it — or pull out all the stops to make sure the child grasps it — based on a sound assessment of what will best serve the child's mathematical development. More than anything, a deep and extensive math background enables the teacher to help a child swiftly and effectively when the child gets stuck. It is almost impossible to turn a math topic swiftly into a series of irresistible and accessible questions unless you have a thorough understanding of the topic and related concepts.

Elementary-level math is a beautiful and useful thing in its own right, but it is also the foundation for algebra and geometry and calculus and number theory and other branches of math. It is much easier to understand the significance of this preparatory stage if one has achieved mastery in areas which build upon this foundation. It is all very well to dismiss parts of math blithely if one has never needed them oneself or has arranged one's life carefully in order to avoid them. "I see no need for long division. It's so dry and grueling. We have calculators now!" is easy to exclaim if one has never had occasion to divide polynomials.

Children are most likely to develop a deep love of math if they are taught by someone who loves and understands math. In some ways, the depth of an elementary or middle school teacher's understanding and love of math is even more critical than a high school teacher's, though of course high school teachers should have solid math backgrounds as well. It is in the early years of school that children develop their math identity and come to either love or loathe math. A high school student who is mathematically adept and confident and finds herself in an Algebra 2 class in which the teacher's explanations are vague and confusing might be able to get on Khan Academy and watch Khan's videos or seek out a knowledgeable person for help, study the textbook carefully, and triumph over the difficult situation. (Many, though, would simply fail the class.)

A six-year-old or a nine-year-old, presented with confusing math, is more likely to conclude, "This is an awful subject. I hate it!" or, "I can't understand this. I'm no good at math," and leave it at that. A young child is unlikely to be able to reflect on the bad experience and put it in context, telling herself, as a confident sixteen-year-old with a solid math background might, "This is being taught in a really confusing way but that doesn't mean math *itself* is confusing … I will figure this out on my own and do it in a way that makes sense to me … even if I correctly solve the problems in a way the teacher does not accept, at least I will understand the material." It is far more likely the younger child will either come to believe she is bad at math, or that math itself is bad.

For these reasons, I strongly urge anyone who is going into elementary or middle or high school math teaching to take as many rigourous high school math classes as possible, followed by a wide selection of university-level math classes (though the math department, not the education department).

32

WHEN THE MATH TEACHER HAS A WEAK MATH BACKGROUND

The reality is that there are thousands of teachers teaching math who have not taken calculus or number theory or abstract algebra. Many elementary-level math teachers would not be able to pass a high school algebra test.

What is the most practical solution to this?

In the long run, raising the math requirements for prospective teachers would be an excellent plan. This would involve requiring that elementary-level math teachers, as part of their training, earn an A in at least Algebra 1, Algebra 2 and Geometry (or the equivalent of these classes), Pre-calculus, and Calculus. I don't think a prospective teacher should be prevented from becoming a teacher for earning a B (or lower) in one of these math classes. Instead, she should be allowed to take the course again and replace the lower grade with a higher one if she does better in the class or she should be allowed to achieve full mastery of all the topics on Khan Academy.

The point of requiring true mastery rather than a passing grade is not to eliminate people who have to work hard at math to understand it (these people might even make better teachers), but rather to ensure that all new teachers have the direct personal experience of fully understanding the material, whether this is hard or easy for them, rather than the experience of failing to understand significant portions of the math and giving up on those.

Why does it matter if an elementary teacher received a B or a C in Algebra? It matters because this means she was confused by as much as 20 to 30% of the material. This is significant. If the teacher struggled with algebra and only managed to learn 60% of it, or 80% of it, her chances of being able to explain math in a clear way drop sharply, as does her conviction that it is possible for a student to master math topics even if they seem very hard at first.

A teacher who gave up on learning algebra when still confused by significant portions of it is likely to have lower expectations for her students — especially students who remind her of her own struggles.

When we give up on students mastering math, we severely narrow their options. A wide variety of rewarding careers are ruled out, and we also leave students vulnerable to being mathematically exploited. People who do not understand math can end up with crushing credit card debt or variable rate mortgages with payments they cannot meet. They can agree to financial terms that sound manageable or even favourable to them, only to find themselves buried in debt or losing their homes. We owe it to children never to give up on their ability to grasp math; the cost is simply too high.

Let's consider the example of Mrs. Anderson, a fourth- grade teacher. Back when Mrs. Anderson was in high school, math was by far the hardest subject she encountered. She barely passed algebra and never took a class beyond this level, not because she is lacking in intelligence, but because the class was badly taught and confusing and there was no support at home to learn it there instead of in the classroom.

When asked about this, she explains, "I was pretty good at math in elementary school but when I got to seventh grade, it stopped making sense. Things got even worse in eighth grade when we started algebra. The teacher talked too fast and most of it did not click with me … I squeaked by somehow, I think because the teacher liked me, but there were all sorts of things I know I never understood. I still have nightmares about having to take a test on the quadratic formula."

Like most teachers, Mrs. Anderson's workday is intense, takes a great deal of energy, and often spills over into the evening. The thought of taking algebra and geometry and calculus at night sounds overwhelming. She uses the latter part of her evenings to unwind a bit and tries to go to bed by ten thirty so she is not exhausted when her alarm goes off at six in the morning.

Even so, she wants to do the best possible job teaching math to her class. She wants her students to like math and do well in it.

What could she do differently tomorrow morning in math class?

Rather than trying to conceal her weak math background from her students and remain at about a sixth or seventh-grade level in math herself, Mrs. Anderson could decide to learn math during the school day with her students.

Teachers are quite willing to read the news with their students without having read it beforehand, or visit a museum with their students and take it in with eyes as fresh as their students'. No teacher would think of pretending she was already quite familiar with the exhibits and knew all the concepts that the exhibits were designed to convey. The same is true of an art museum.

Yet with math, there is often shame, and with that shame comes a cover-up. Teachers are reluctant to admit they don't know things about math because they think it will make them look poorly educated or lacking in intelligence. The fact that these teachers may have graduated from excellent universities with degrees in education does not really help much with this; however high their GPAs and impressive their resumes, they may still feel discomfort if they are hazy on the math concepts they are trying to teach.

I suggest that teachers bravely take the same attitude toward math that they might take at a hands-on science museum they are visiting with their students. Even if teachers cannot (initially) be models of mathematical competence and expertise, they *can* be models of openness to learning, self-discipline, intellectual curiosity, persistence in the face of difficulty and confusion, willingness to make mistakes while learning (an absolute essential in math), and excitement about the subject. They can openly learn math along with their students and model keenness and determination. This is far, far better than remaining at a safe distance, giving out assignments that are too easy and boring for the children, or, alternatively, giving harder work which is full of concepts the teacher can't clearly explain. This approach, of learning with the students, takes humility, but as humility is one of the highest virtues, this is yet another powerful modeling.

Suppose, for example, Ms. Anderson is called over in class by a student who is stumped by a problem in the textbook. Ms. Anderson reads the problem and does not know how to solve it. Now what?

She can hide this and say, "If that problem is too hard for you, go back to the previous section and redo some of the problems," or, "You need to learn how to make better use of your textbook explanations. Read the section carefully that comes right before those problems and then try that problem again."

Alternatively, she could respond by saying, "I'm not sure how to solve this one either. Let's try to figure it out together." This is the braver and more productive approach. She can then begin to model good problem-solving skills even though she does not know how to solve this particular problem. She can start by saying, "Let's read the question again very carefully," and read it aloud. She can make suggestions that demonstrate how to approach a problem one does not immediately see how to solve.

She could say, "When we just read the problem carefully, I realized that the first stumbling block for me is that I do not remember what a rhombus is. I know it's a four-sided shape but I can't remember exactly what type. Do you remember the definition of a rhombus or should we look it up?" (Isolate a term one needs to know in order to solve the problem but has forgotten or never learned.) From there she could go on trying to make sense of the problem with the child. "Okay, now we know what a rhombus is. Let's read the problem again. When I get stuck and am not sure how to move on, I sometimes find it helpful to draw a picture of the problem…"

Of course it would have been most efficient if the teacher had instantly known how to solve the problem and been able to ask the student precisely the questions that would have brought about swift understanding, but there is still a great deal of value in admitting confusion and modeling how to confront this and move through it. The ability to do this is a very valuable skill. Strong math students practice this all the time rather than giving up or writing down a guess.

A teacher who jumps in and learns with her students will get better and better at math, and as she gets better, she will come to like math more and more. All three of these qualities — a willingness to plunge in and solve a problem one is puzzled by, persistence, and an enjoyment of math — will be transferred to the students.

Another thing a teacher can do is to work on Khan Academy herself, creating her own learning goals, solidifying her understanding of critical topics, reviewing things not practiced in recent years, and moving into unfamiliar territory. Being immersed in the learning of math makes for better teaching. It makes one more empathetic to the challenges and frustrations that one's students are up against. It deepens one's understanding of the subject. It familiarizes one with other ways of presenting topics. Devoting even an hour every weekend to working on Khan Academy would make a significant difference.

33

ENGAGING YOUNG CHILDREN WHO CAN'T SIT STILL

There are many perfectly healthy and normal young children, especially little boys in the very early elementary years, who find it almost impossible to sit still and focus on work they do not find engaging. Though some young children genuinely do have psychiatric disorders which may require both medication and therapy, there are many children who simply need the math lesson to be tailored to their needs rather than having their brain chemistry tailored to fit the math lesson.

Most children, if given math that is truly interesting, will sit at their desks for long periods, completely engrossed. For young children who feel the pressing need to move and physically explore rather than sit relatively still, more hands-on math should be offered. For those who simply cannot yet sit still, perhaps because they are not developmentally ready to, there should be an unlimited supply of math challenges provided which allow the child to engage physically with the math (more physically than writing or typing). This would include 3-dimensional math puzzles, games that have meaningful and stimulating mathematical content, and constructing things such as polyhedra which rely on mathematical thinking.

It is better to engage young children in a hands-on kind of math they thoroughly enjoy than to medicate them into doing a kind of math they are not yet suited to. We simply do not know the long-term effects of putting small children on amphetamines. We do, however, know that early joyful hands-on educational experiences have lasting value. The latter, then, seems far less risky for children who respond to this means of getting them to focus and learn.

Children mature at different rates and develop the capacity to focus on written work at different ages. I have known children who loved to sit still and concentrate on written work for several hours at a time at the startlingly young age of three; I have also known many seven-year-olds who find it hard to sit still for even five minutes unless they are deeply engaged.

The key is to find mathematically rich activities that suit the child. One six-year-old might enjoy figuring out mathematical sequences and writing subsequent terms and want to solve a variety of problems of this type for an hour; another six-year-old might want to do this for a few minutes and then would feel restless if pressed to stick with it.

Math class should be adapted to allow young children to learn in ways that match their development. As always, joy and deep learning should be the primary goals. A young child who is busily constructing a set of polyhedra, testing and seeing if he can make a closed 3-dimensional shape entirely out of triangles, then squares, then pentagons, and finally hexagons, will learn much more than he would if he were medicated and told to do three pages of addition problems, and he will come away from this polyhedra exploration loving math.

This is not to say that no child needs medication — but if the primary reason for medicating the child is so he can focus on work he does not find interesting and sit still when he is not yet ready to, the first thing that should be explored is whether this child's inattentiveness and resistance and educational plateauing disappear when he is offered a kind of math that is both valuable and suits his current level of development.

The teacher's job is to know her students deeply enough to recognize the needs of each and maintain a classroom atmosphere and degree of focus that is conducive to a variety of kinds of learning. This involves teaching the children to be aware of their classmates, considerate of others, and not to distract anyone. A child who is sitting at a table deeply absorbed in designing and making polyhedra will not distract a child who is solving equations nearby. However, children who are talking about things other than math, or throwing things, or wandering around aimlessly, will most certainly undermine the focus of the room.

I never allow random chit chat in a math class, or any other activity that seems distracting, even when I am not standing at the board teaching the entire class. I immediately refocus any child I notice creating even a small distraction. I provide plenty of leeway for children to stare into space thinking, or conduct an experiment to test an idea, or request harder work or easier work. I'm very strict when it comes to anyone disturbing anyone else's learning, and not strict at all when it comes to someone working in an unconventional way, as long as the child is focused and learning and not distracting anyone else.

34

HOMEWORK

Young children should not be required to do homework. After a day in school, elementary-aged children should be free to play and enjoy their families and friends, to pursue their interests and passions, to relax, explore, daydream, and simply enjoy life. If a school day is well spent and productive, there is no need to force a child to spend more hours on school work, though of course any child who wants to do math for pleasure at home should be provided with an ample supply of interesting problems and math puzzles and games.

In about sixth or seventh grade, homework should be gradually introduced, but it should not exceed an hour a day. Instead, both teachers and parents should expose children to activities that may spark a passion in the child, and then those passions should be supported. A child who loves chess should be offered a chess board and the opportunity to join a chess club. A child who loves to write poetry should be offered the kind of peace that is conducive to this, as well as outstanding and inspiring poems by others (not to write long forced essays about, but simply to savour).

Even though research has shown that homework does not benefit young children, many teachers and schools still feel they must insist upon it. Perhaps the single greatest cost of homework is the stress and conflict it often results in at home. What is the best way for a parent to minimize or avoid this with an elementary-aged child?

One approach, which would only work for a certain kind of child, is the one my mother took. Not once during my entire childhood did my mother ever ask me if I had any homework or if I had done my homework. My homework was treated as entirely my own business. If for some reason I had not done it, this was thought of a matter between me and my teacher (not between me and my mother). It was taken for granted that if I forgot to do it, I would have to face the music at school — but it certainly was not going to become a point of contention at home. Naturally, this method would only work with a child who cared about displeasing the teacher and who also felt that the teacher's authority should be respected. This approach made me feel completely responsible for my own homework. I did not delegate it in my mind to my mother and then forget about it until she told me to do it and then argue that I was not ready to do it. Making things much easier was the fact that the private school I went to from age five to age ten, though extremely academically rigourous, never had more than a few minutes of homework a day for children my age. In the public elementary school I went to for grades six and seven, there was still very little homework. By the time I had any meaningful amount of homework, I was a teenager and perfectly capable of managing my own time. I have no memories of not doing my homework. I just did it automatically, and on my own, like getting dressed or brushing my teeth or making my breakfast.

There are schools, though, that have two hours of required homework a day by second grade. A seven-year-old who might have been perfectly capable of figuring out the best time to do ten minutes of homework and sit down and do it on his own might be utterly overwhelmed if the homework was intended to take two hours, especially if he did not get home from after-school care until dinner time.

My suggestion for a parent who has the time for this is to make yourself available to do the math homework with your child if he is confused or overwhelmed by it, or even if he just wants your company after a day apart. This may sound counterproductive. How will a child learn to do it on his own? How will he learn the concepts? How will he become responsible and independent?

These qualities are more likely to develop if you sit down at the table with him and dive into the problems together, viewing them as a challenge the two of you can meet. Do not do the problems for him. Instead, figure them out together, having your child do every single part he is able to.

Turn what could have been a two-hour-long struggle with him putting his head down and crying and you badgering and cajoling him, and him trying again and getting frustrated, and you admonishing him and threatening consequences, and him trying to escape, and you telling him to sit back down, into an enjoyable, satisfying, efficient joint problem-solving session.

If he is asked to answer twenty questions involving multiplying fractions and he doesn't know how to begin, don't ask him whether he was paying attention in class or tell him to find a video online that explains it or insist that he search through his textbook to find the page that shows how to do it. Instead, do the first one for him, showing him clearly exactly how. Then ask him to do the next. If he gets it and can rapidly do them all, let him charge through them on his own while you start making dinner nearby.

If he is then asked to solve word problems he does not know how to start on, do the first one with him, asking him questions you know he can answer and eliciting from him as much of the solution as you can. "So, how much money does Joe have to start with? Let's look back to the first sentence …" Use the textbook as a resource rather than an admonition. If your child is not adept at finding information in it, involve him in the search. "What would you call this kind of problem? … Let's look that up in the index …" is much more helpful than, "The book must have explained it somewhere."

Math is often learned best when a teacher or parent or peer shows the child how to solve particular kind of problem, then does a very similar one together with the child, and then asks the child to do the next few independently with the work being checked, the effort praised, and further help offered if some part of the process is being done wrong.

Doing math in this efficient and enjoyable way does not make a child dependent or lazy. Rather, it shows the child that math can be very fun, and that homework can be done quite swiftly, and that their parent cares about their learning and wants to spend time with them.

A child who has understood the homework and mastered the concepts involved is far more likely to pay attention in class in the coming days, so parents should not fear that working with their children in this manner will lead their children to become lazy and detached in the classroom. Naturally, this approach to homework will only work out if it goes smoothly and happily. If it creates or increases conflict between parent and child, it is better to keep parental involvement in homework to a bare minimum.

What about in middle and high school? I still recommend this very same method. If the child is able to do all the homework independently and understands it all or can figure it out on his own, then let him get on with it. But suppose a child is struggling with a concept in algebra or geometry or pre-calculus or calculus. If you know how to do it, jump in and do it together with the goal of getting your child to deeply understand it and be able to do it without you. If you don't remember how to do it but feel you could quickly get the skill back by reviewing a bit, still jump in and learn the concept together.

As with younger children, this approach of working with your child should only be used if it does not lead to arguments and stress. If you have no idea how to do it and don't think you can readily figure it out, encourage your child to find similar problems on Khan Academy and look at the hints or the accompanying videos (with or without you) or go over examples in the textbook. If your child is still confused, it can be very helpful to enlist the help of a family member or friend who knows the material or hire a tutor.

The point of your helping is to increase the chances that your child will enjoy math, make your child more competent and confident at problem-solving, and deepen your bond with your child.

It is also helpful to let your children see you actively learning and doing your own "homework" of a type that is similar to theirs (reading books, researching areas of interest, writing — in other words, actively learning).

Having areas in the home that are conducive to learning and working will encourage these activities. For young children, an example of this might be a large wooden table with a jar of pencils (regular and coloured) and a ruler, and a container of Cuisenaire rods. Nearby, on a set of shelves, could be stacks of paper, watercolour paints, art pads, math puzzles and games, and a chess set. Children are more likely to sit down and learn if the supplies they need are right there and don't need to be searched for, and if the set-up is spacious and inviting. A Snap Circuits kit or a Meccano set, tucked tidily away on a high shelf, will not be played with nearly as much as one that is kept beside a smooth, flat surface (such as an inviting table, or a clear area of floor). A chess set that is set up at one end of a long dining room table will likely be played with hundreds of times more than one that is down at the bottom of a toy box.

35

EMBEDDING COMPUTERIZED LEARNING IN A RICHLY COMMUNICATIVE CLASSROOM

No matter how superbly designed a computerized math program is, it cannot replace human interaction, paper and pencils, and hands-on math. Khan Academy is the most outstanding online learning site I have ever found — and it is most powerful when children make use of it in the context of real-life human connection.

Children need grounding in a world that is solid and has boundaries because this helps impart a sense of meaning to what they are learning. When a child spends too many hours at a screen, even doing meaningful work, he can become lost in this and disconnected from what matters most. This virtual world can seem, paradoxically, both compelling and meaningless if too much time is spent there.

Something different takes place when a child asks a person for help rather than clicking on an explanatory video on the screen. Holding and opening a beautiful book is not the same as clicking on screens. All these things — the real-life discussions, the online videos, the questions on the screen and the questions in books — are valuable. For children to stay healthy and balanced, they need to be offered a full range of learning experiences.

We want to sensitize children to the subtleties of conversation, to the give and take of explaining and absorbing. We want to help them develop the tremendously important skills of listening intently (even in the face of disagreement), of formulating the right questions to move from confusion to clarity, of experiencing and showing interest in other people and their ideas, of sharing their insights and thoughts in ways that draw other people in. We want children to learn how to convey respect and openness so they can contribute. We want them to develop a willingness to connect with, help, and be helped by others.

Some of these skills are dependent on eye contact, tone of voice, understanding how close to stand to another person, how close to draw up one's chair, what kinds of words to use to set someone else at ease, how loudly or softly to speak, and when to fall silent and listen.

Computers are remarkably useful in the classroom because they allow one teacher to offer thirty children math at precisely their level with the built-in immediate feedback that is so important to learning math. This tool should be used at all the right times — but we should be aware of both its power and its limitations. In addition to giving children access to a vast wealth of math on a screen, we want to encourage children to experience the aesthetic pleasure of solving equations or creating geometric proofs on paper.

Children also need the experience of solving problems with solid objects they move around and manipulate and create order with. This stimulates different processes in the brain. Moving objects through space helps develop depth perception in a way that does not take place when a child exclusively solves problems on a flat screen that is typically a set distance away from the eyes.

factoring quadratics using Cuisenaire rods

36

FINDING A BALANCE

The best way to inspire a class of children to love math and reach their full potential is to listen to them carefully, understand their varied needs, and offer them a balance of all the elements that make for intense and joyful learning.

Every child should be offered an unlimited number of engaging problems at the right level. The simplest and most efficient way to determine this level and gain access to problems at this precise level is by having the children make use of Khan Academy.

In addition to this, there should be group problem solving, led by the teacher at the board, using problems that are accessible and meaningful to the entire class. The teacher should directly and explicitly teach problem-solving techniques and concepts, asking as many questions as possible to keep the children actively engaged. This kind of carefully orchestrated group work is an ideal time for the teacher to both model and make explicit how to communicate superbly.

When not teaching the whole class at the board, the teacher should offer one-on-one or small group instruction involving eye contact, questioning, and conversation.

In addition to math problems on Khan Academy, there should

be problems on paper which are designed to further open up children to the beauty of algebra, geometry, number theory, topology, and logic. Having the problems on paper encourages children to draw more, create more visual solutions, and share their insights more readily with interested classmates.

The classroom, ideally, should have a great supply of 3-dimensional math manipulatives to aid in math explorations and problem-solving, as well as math games and puzzles to stimulate and inspire the children.

Though it is a bit of a well-kept secret, there are few things in life more enjoyable than teaching math to children, and bringing together all these crucial elements makes all the difference.

APPENDIX 1: HOW TO STRUCTURE AN ENGAGING MATH CLASS FOR CHILDREN

Part 1: Hands-on math puzzles and games (10 minutes)

Set out a wide variety of math puzzles and games and allow the children ten minutes to work on these. This can include individual puzzles like Rush Hour, Chocolate Fix, Tower of Hanoi, Block by Block, Brick Logic, tangrams, as well as 2 - 4 person math strategy games like Pentago, Q-bitz, Blokus, or Othello which children can team up to play.

Part 2: Whole group learning, led by teacher (10 - 15 minutes)

Lead the children in a discussion/exploration of a math topic which will be both accessible and challenging to the entire class.

Examples would be a deductive logic problem or a math topic which will deepen the knowledge or skills of everyone present.

Have everyone quietly face the board. Desks should be arranged so no one has her back or shoulder to the board and everyone has a clear view.

Use a discovery approach (lots and lots of questions designed to guide the children toward understanding). Involve every student and elicit feedback frequently from all the students.

Part 3: Individual problem solving (30 - 60 minutes)

Have everyone work on problems at their own level and pace, using a combination of Khan Academy (if tablets or computers are available) and workbooks or photo-copied problem sets or textbook problems.

Manipulatives such as Cuisenaire rods or patterns blocks or polyhedra should be offered if they are available and will further the children's understanding.

As the children work, walk around the room offering help to anyone who wants it. Allow and encourage students to help each other.

If several people seem to need help on the same problem or concept, invite them to gather at a table close to the board and teach them together, asking lots of questions and guiding them toward a clear understanding.

Part 4: Memorization (optional) (5 minutes)

If the class is at the stage of memorizing addition facts or times tables, have them devote five minutes to concentrated memorization. This can take the form of using an online trainer/prompter, or testing each other in pairs using Cuisenaire rod arrays or flash cards or multiplication clocks, or briskly doing pages of math facts.

This memorization period can also be used to memorize definitions or formulae relevant to what each child is studying so they will become more efficient problem-solvers, able to focus more easily on concepts and strategy rather than getting bogged down in computation or looking up things that will be needed repeatedly for years to come.

Examples of things that should be memorized include: formulae for finding the area of rectangles, triangles, and circles; algorithms for performing operations on fractions; rules for working with exponents. (Please note that terms and definitions and formulae should not be memorized without a basic understanding of what they mean and concepts should never be memorized but should instead be understood and mastered.)

Each child should have a set of index cards of facts or definitions or algorithms they are currently committing to memory and these should be consulted when the teacher announces that five minutes will be devoted to memorization.
Unless the class happens to be made of up children who are all at the same level (a very rare situation), this memorization time should be individualized so students are memorizing exactly what they need for their stage of development. Some children might be memorizing the fives times tables while other might be memorizing formulae for the volume of cylinders and cones.

APPENDIX 2: A SUMMARY OF ARM AND HAND SIGNALS

These signals should be taught to the class at the beginning of the first lesson so the children can provide feedback to the teacher whenever the teacher is presenting math at the board. The teacher should swiftly review them at the start of each class until they become automatic to everyone in the class.

• **"I agree."** (Pumping arms.)
• **"I disagree."** (Scissoring arms.)
• **"I partly agree and partly disagree."** (One arm pumping and the other doing a sideways motion.)
• **"I don't know."** (Hands held palms up.)
• **"Stolen answer."** (One hand grabbing fistfuls of air.)
• **"Stop! I'm confused!"** (One hand held in a stop sign, the other held palm up, eyebrows raised.)
• **"Stop! I have a question."** (One hand up, the other pushed forward.) This combination of arm signals is more urgent that simply having a question and indicates the child must ask the question immediately in order to follow what is being said.
• **"Confusion breaker."** (Meaning, "I can clear up the confu-

sion," and shown with a silent snapping forward of the arms as if to break a thin sheet of ice.)

- **"I'm starting to understand."** (One lightbulb, formed with thumb and forefinger, held over the head.)
- **"I really understand."** (Two lightbulbs held over the head.)
- **"I've had a total breakthrough!"** (Two bouncing lightbulbs held over the head.)
- **"I have a question."** (One arm and hand curved in a question mark, the other hand in a fist below. The bottom hand can alternate between being the dot at the bottom of the question mark and pointing to the person the child wants to question, or a circling motion indicating a desire to pose a question to the whole class.)
- **"I have a theory to propose."** (Arms forming a big "T".)
- **"Please repeat your last statement."** (Both hands making a gesture toward oneself.)
- **"Please turn up the volume."** (A twisting motion with one hand to indicate that one cannot hear what is being said.)
- **"I can't see the board."** (Flat hands moving back and forth over eyes.)
- **"Algebra applause."** (Vigourous silent clapping, with the palms not quite touching, to indicate appreciation of someone else's great idea or insight or explanation.)
- **"I just changed my mind."** (Fingers of both hands touching temples, then shifting sideways, as if a set of thoughts has just been moved out of the mind.)

In addition, students should be asked to use their fingers (or arms) to show:

- **numbers**
- **operations** (addition, subtraction, multiplication, division)
- **directions**
- **shapes**
- **brackets**

ABOUT THE AUTHOR

Jane Molnar's career has been dedicated to inspiring mathematical confidence, competence, and joy in children.

She developed a love of math at age five at Miss Edgar's and Miss Cramp's School for Girls in Montreal and went on to study mathematics at Cariboo College (now Thompson Rivers University), the University of Victoria, and the University of Washington.

She has taught math in twenty elementary and middle schools in Berkeley, Oakland, and Richmond and in the MESA program at UC Berkeley.

She had trained mathematicians, scientists, engineers, and public-school teachers to teach math to children using a guided discovery approach.

She lives in Berkeley, California where she divides her time between writing, private math tutoring of elementary and middle school children, and enjoying her family and friends.

For more information, please visit janemolnar.com.

Made in the USA
Lexington, KY
20 August 2019